J. GORDON VAETH is Manager of the TIROS Operational Satellite System Engineering Division, National Weather Satellite Center, United States Weather Bureau. Previously he served the Advanced Research Projects Agency in the Department of Defense as Technical Staff Member for Man-in-Space, and was Head of the New Weapons and Systems Division, United States Naval Training Device Center. His published papers and articles include contributions to the *Encyclopaedia Britannica*. Mr. Vaeth is author of *200 Miles Up*, published by The Ronald Press Company.

WEATHER EYES IN THE SKY

America's Meteorological Satellites

J. GORDON VAETH

NATIONAL WEATHER SATELLITE CENTER
UNITED STATES WEATHER BUREAU

THE RONALD PRESS COMPANY · NEW YORK

Library of Congress Catalog Card Number: 65–12760

To

the scientists, engineers, technicians, and management personnel of NASA, the Weather Bureau, and industry who together made the weather satellite dream of the 1950's into the reality of today.

Preface

The overall story of the weather satellites has not heretofore been pieced together and told for the general public. This book attempts to accomplish this in three parts.

Part I is a summary of the evolution of weather-observing techniques in America. Part II pictorially describes the TIROS and Nimbus satellites and their role in meteorology. Part III considers the nature of things to come.

It has been said that the weather satellite program is the most useful of all United States space efforts. In the pages that follow, the reader-taxpayer may reach his own conclusion as to whether this is indeed the case.

To the following persons I want particularly to express my appreciation for the help they provided in obtaining information, photographs, and other material for *Weather Eyes in the Sky:*

Mr. Paul E. Lehr, U.S. Weather Bureau
Mr. John C. Nyhan, U.S. Weather Bureau
Mr. Herbert S. Lieb, U.S. Weather Bureau
Mrs. Ann K. Cook, U.S. Weather Bureau
Mr. George H. Winthrop, U.S. Weather Bureau
Mrs. Margaret S. Ware, NASA Headquarters
Mrs. F. Edward Cavin, Radio Corporation of America
Mr. M. J. Schmitt, Republic Aviation Corporation
Mr. Robert H. Hood, Jr., Republic Aviation Corporation
Mr. Robert D. Ladd, G. T. Schjeldahl Company
Mr. E. E. Jungclas, Hughes Aircraft Company

Without their assistance, the writing of this book would not have been possible.

J. Gordon Vaeth

Washington, D.C.
    January, 1965

Contents

WEATHER EYES
IN THE SKY

I

The Beginnings

American interest in observing the weather—an interest that would eventually produce the world's first meteorological satellite—began at least three hundred years ago.

From 1644 to 1645, in Swedes Fort, Delaware, the Reverend John Campanius kept what are believed to have been the first continuous weather records in colonial America.

Benjamin Franklin, whose interest in atmospheric electricity inspired his famous kite-flying experiment, was also an observer of the weather. He noted that major storms were usually preceded by a northeast wind, and he concluded that they moved generally from out of the southwest.

Thomas Jefferson, who would probably have become famous as a scientist had he not been a statesman and President, daily recorded the weather and temperature. The meteorological notes that he compiled were often consulted by others during his lifetime.

In Jefferson's day, some weather instruments already existed and were in fairly widespread use. These included the thermometer, invented by Galileo about 1593, and the mercury barometer, by Torricelli in 1643. Wind vanes, of which a prize example is still to be seen at Jefferson's Monticello home, had been developed in various forms since the days of the ancient Greeks. Rain gages, devices to collect and measure rainfall, had been known in India reportedly as far back as 400 B.C.

Thus, a start toward weather observing had long before been made. There remained the task of taking these observations—and reporting them—on a systematic, organized, and routine basis.

First step in this direction took place in the United States during the War of 1812. Interested in the relationship of weather to health, the Surgeon General of the Army ordered hospital surgeons to begin keeping weather and climatological records. At first this was a directive neither rapidly nor fully complied with. Yet, by the mid-1850's, almost a hundred Army installations were compiling such information.

In the meantime, the invention of the telegraph and the interest in meteorology of Professor Joseph Henry, Secretary of the Smithsonian Institution, combined to create an extensive weather observing and reporting network in 1849. Professor Henry arranged with the telegraph companies to have their stations make simultaneous observations and telegraph the results immediately to the Smithsonian in Washington. In return he would provide these stations and their operators with the necessary weather instruments. By the outbreak of the War Between the States, this network of cooperating telegraph stations had reached five hundred in number, so many that the Smithsonian had difficulty in supplying them with the required observing equipment. From the information provided by these observations, Professor Henry began the preparation and publication of the nation's first weather maps.

EARLY FORECASTS

The War Between the States disrupted the Smithsonian network. Post-hostilities efforts to revive or replace it with a federally supported program failed, at first, to win Congressional support. In the absence of a government program, Cleveland Abbe, Director of the Cincinnati Observatory, initiated a regional network of observing and reporting stations in 1869. With their data, he began issuing forecasts, calling them "probabilities." In Wisconsin, Increase A. Lapham was similarly, but unsuccessfully, attempting the institution of a weather network, one that would provide forecasts and warnings, particularly for shipping on the Great Lakes.

But the weather information needs of the nation, a nation growing geographically, agriculturally, industrially, commercially, and economically, could no longer adequately be met by privately operated, regional networks. Now what was required was a nationwide network, a "national weather service," operated under U.S. government auspices. A resolution that would establish such a service was introduced by Representative H. E. Paine, a Lapham supporter from Wisconsin; was passed by the Forty-first Congress; and was signed by President Grant on February 9, 1870.

To the War Department, and more specifically to its Signal Service (predecessor of the Signal Corps), was the responsibility assigned. The existence of the Army's telegraph system by which weather data could be communicated rapidly between many points within the United States played a not-inconsiderable role in this assignment.

An official publication, describing the meteorological state of things in 1870, lists the following instruments that were in use at that time.

(a) the wind vane, by which wind direction was determined;
(b) the anemometer, a rotating device for the measurement of wind speed;
(c) the rain gage, for measuring precipitation;
(d) the thermometer;
(e) the maximum and minimum thermometer;
(f) the barometer, to determine atmospheric pressure; and
(g) the sling psychrometer, a device with wet and dry bulb thermometers to measure the amount of moisture or humidity in the air.

FIRST AIRBORNE MEASUREMENTS

Perhaps the most noticeable things about these instruments is that they were all surface-observation-type devices. Weather reports of the 1870's, and for the twenty-five years or so to follow, were limited to what the observer could measure or see from the earth's surface.

Research on clouds, for example, was carried out from mountaintop stations, such as the one on Mount Washington (6,288 feet) in New Hampshire. Airborne experiments, from which rocket and satellite observations would eventually derive, were quite slow in coming.

They began during the 1870's and 1880's in the form of a limited number of manned free balloon flights. Made for strictly research purposes, these ascents measured such variables as temperature and humidity in relationship to altitude. One of the experimenters, Professor H. A. Hazen, wanted to extend these flights to include a transatlantic crossing.[1] Although of some value for research and experi-

---

[1] Despite the subsequent passage of three-quarters of a century, no America-to-Europe manned balloon flight has ever been made. Yet the idea persists. During 1964, two groups were attempting separately to raise support for such a venture.

mentation, these ascents were too sporadic, isolated, and costly to be of use for routine observing. A better means of making airborne measurements was required. To find it, weathermen would next turn their attention to kites.

Before they did, however, major organizational changes would be made in the national weather service. Following a rash of complaints about the military's way of running things, legislation was enacted transferring it from the Army Signal Service to the Department of Agriculture. The transfer date was July 1, 1891. The part of the Department that was to perform this function was named the U.S. Weather Bureau.

Four years later, in 1895, Professor Charles F. Marvin, one of the new Bureau's most creative members and later to become its Chief, began experimenting with box kites. An inventor of many types of weather instruments, he designed and built what he called his kite meteorograph. Carried aloft it measured and recorded temperature, pressure, humidity, and wind speed at kite altitudes above the ground (Fig. 1).

Fig. 1. With box kites such as this, the Weather Bureau made some of its earliest attempts to observe the upper air. (U.S. Weather Bureau photo.)

It was soon discovered that to place a meteorograph-equipped kite at a thousand feet necessitated a windspeed of at least 10–15 miles per hour. The use of kites was, therefore, critically dependent upon winds. They showed such an advantage over manned free balloons, however, that despite their shortcomings the Weather Bureau opened sixteen kite stations during 1898. Over the years that followed, and until 1933 when the program was ended, kite observations were carried out at various levels of effort and at various levels of altitude.

A tandem arrangement was used in which as many as six or eight kites were employed. The topmost carried the Marvin meteorograph. Steel piano wire was used, the weight of which served to limit the altitude that could be attained. As a rule this amounted to about 8,000 feet. One kite, launched in Virginia on October 3, 1907, is reported to have reached 23,111 feet.

Kite flying was not without its difficulties. Mechanical winches were used to reel in the thousands of feet of wire stretching between ground and sky. (Altitude was determined by the length of wire payed out and by its elevation angle.) Sometimes the line broke and the kite would take off cross-country, its wire dangling beneath.

Despite many successful flights, kites showed themselves too wind-sensitive and affected by rain for use in routine observations from several stations simultaneously. Still another way to obtain upper-air measurements would have to be developed. So balloons were looked at again.

Small tethered balloons: they could be let up on light lines at times when winds were too weak for kite flying. They made possible observations to an average altitude of 6,500 feet. Like the kites, they were essentially limited to heights relatively close to the ground.

And free or untethered balloons: tracked by optical means, they provided valuable information on wind direction and speed at the various altitudes that they traversed. In time these became known as *pibals* or pilot balloons (Fig. 2). During 1909 a number of these were launched, of which eight reached heights of 10 miles or better.

It was not long before weathermen began to attach instrument packages to these balloons, in short to convert them to sounding balloons. Successful experiments along this line had, in fact, been underway in Europe for some time, particularly by the Frenchman Teisserenc de Bort. Sounding balloons were sent aloft by the

Fig. 2. A scene that now belongs to history: the nighttime launch of a pilot balloon (pibal) with a candle and lantern attached. In 1938, when this picture was taken, candles were used to enable observers to keep sight of the balloon while it was being tracked. Today a small battery-powered light is used. (U.S. Weather Bureau photo.)

Weather Bureau in 1910 from Omaha, Nebraska, and Huron, South Dakota. One of those from Huron climbed to almost 19 miles.

The Bureau's sounding balloon flights were experimental and non-routine. Each balloon carried a meteorograph and a parachute, the latter to bring the instrument package safely back to earth following bursting of the balloon at ceiling altitude. Useful results required, of course, that the meteorograph physically be recovered for analysis of its record. Thus, availability of the observations was subject to delays of hours, days, weeks, or even longer. Sometimes the instrument package was never found. As long as this uncertainty about data recovery continued, sounding balloons could hardly be considered suitable for systematic and operational use.

During World War I, kites and pilot balloons were utilized as were some tethered and sounding balloons. In 1919–1920 the Chief of the Weather Bureau attempted to expand the upper-air program through the increased use of kites, pilot balloons, and sounding balloons and with the addition of airplane observations. His efforts met with Congressional opposition and defeat.

In 1925, however, the Weather Bureau and the Navy began a cooperative program of airplane observations at the Naval Air Station, Anacostia, in Washington, D.C. For a brief period, daily flights were made at 8:00 A.M. to about 10,000 feet with a Marvin meteorograph secured atop the upper wing. After each flight, the data recorded by the instrument, plus the pilot's own observations, were speeded to the local Weather Bureau forecast office.

Six years would elapse, however, before airplane observations— they came to be known as *apobs*—would be undertaken on a routine basis (Fig. 3). At Cleveland, Chicago, Omaha, and Dallas, pilots took off under Weather Bureau contract to carry meteorographs to heights of 13,500 feet or greater. To make these early morning flights, they were paid $25, provided that they reached the 13,500-foot designated minimum altitude. For every additional 1,000 feet attained, they received a bonus of 10 per cent.

The systematic introduction of these airplane observations in 1931 administered the coup de grâce to the Weather Bureau's kite program, which was terminated two years later. During 1937 apobs were flown from a total of thirty fields. Army and Navy pilots carried aloft the meteorographs from seventeen of these; civilian pilots under contract to the Bureau from the remaining thirteen. By 1938 these contract pilots were being required to reach 16,500 feet in order to qualify for their pay. This demand for higher observations was not without its dangers to both military and civilian airmen. Lack of oxygen and other flight hazards took the lives of twelve of them between 1931 and 1938.

Fig. 3. An *apob* (airplane observation) in process of being made. Note the recording meteorograph attached to the wing struts. In flying this mission, it was important to maintain a fairly constant rate of climb. (U.S. Weather Bureau photo.)

The Army was the first to discontinue the making of apobs for the Weather Bureau. It considered that such flights interfered excessively with military missions. Its monoplanes, furthermore, could not as satisfactorily mount and carry the meteorograph as could the Navy's biplanes. These latter continued to fly such weather-data-gathering assignments for about one more year. By the beginning of World War II, the routine taking of basic measurements for the Weather Bureau by service airplanes had about reached its end.

THE RADIOSONDE AND RADAR

A new development had come about that made such flights unnecessary. Radio had been married to the sounding balloon. It was no longer necessary to search for, locate, and recover the meteorograph package in order to obtain the observational data. A radio transmitter would convey this information to the ground while the balloon was in flight.

Scientists of several countries had sought to develop and perfect such a radio meteorograph. The first to achieve this was a Russian, Professor P. A. Moltchanoff, about 1928. Three years later he gave a vivid demonstration of the potentialities of this device by launching three radio meteorograph balloons from the dirigible GRAF ZEPPELIN while it cruised above the Arctic Ocean. The widespread adoption of the Moltchanoff-type balloon by the United States and other nations took place through the 1930's (Fig. 4). In 1938 the term "radio meteorograph" was replaced by "radiosonde." The observations that it provided were called *raobs*.

The radio-equipped sounding balloon saw extensive use during World War II as meteorologists attempted to keep their observing and reporting [2] ability current with the weather information demands of air, land, and sea combat.

Because radiosondes measure and report only temperature, pressure, and humidity, other techniques had to be employed if they were to provide wind information as well. They could, of course, be tracked optically in azimuth and elevation like a pilot balloon. This, plus knowledge of their rate of ascent, would enable wind direction and speed to be calculated. Visual tracking was obviously impossible when the balloons were in or above the clouds. To overcome this and to make possible "all weather" tracking of radiosondes, techniques were developed (1) to use a direction-finder on the radio signal emitted by the rising balloon and (2) to range on the balloon by radar. (This latter approach required a special type balloon or balloon-borne reflector to insure adequate radar signal return.) A radiosonde-equipped balloon from which wind information is obtained by either of these means is called a *rawinsonde*.

---

[2] The growth in the weather community's ability to report or communicate its information has been almost as impressive as the development of its observing capability. In this growth, the telegraph, tele.hone, radio link, and teletype have played major roles.

Fig. 4. An early Moltchanoff-type balloon, predecessor of today's radio-sonde. (U.S. Weather Bureau photo.)

The electronic technology inspired by the war provided weather-men with the capability of using surveillance radar for the detection and tracking of severe storms. War-surplus radars were quickly applied by the Weather Bureau [3] to the task of squall line and tornado detection in the Midwest and of hurricane detection and tracking along the Atlantic and Gulf coasts.

The Bureau has had this to say about the value of radar as an observational tool:

By maintaining a close watch of the radarscope, the radar observer can determine the direction and speed of movement of areas of precipitation. Also he can ascertain whether the storm is increasing or decreasing in intensity and area coverage. Often the type of precipitation particles can be distinguished. . . . Certain storms have their own characteristic rainfall patterns, and a corresponding characteristic appearance on the radarscope, such as the spiral band echo pattern characteristic of tropical hurricanes or the "hook" echo associated with some tornadoes.

One of the most valuable uses of weather radars is to detect and track severe storms, such as hurricanes and tornadoes, at great distances over inaccessible areas for long periods, thus increasing the chance for advance warning to the public. For example, the eye of Hurricane "Carla" (September, 1961) first appeared on the Weather Bureau's radarscope at Galveston, Texas when it was located 220 nautical miles to the south over the Gulf of Mexico, and was continuously tracked by this radar for 46 hours. Severe local storms, such as tornadoes, are more limited in extent than hurricanes, and may often develop, run their course, and dissipate without being observed visually by either a weather observer or the public (this is particularly true at night). The weather radar covers an area of surveillance on the order of 200,000 square miles, and continuous day and night surveillance is possible.

Hurricanes, of course, are also observed by weather reconnaissance aircraft that fly into their interiors to collect information of both a research and operational nature. The aircrews making these flights can obtain radiosonde-type observations vertically beneath the plane by releasing a parachute-equipped instrument package. This radiosonde-in-reverse is not unexpectedly known as a dropsonde.

Aircraft also investigate the nature of severe local storms. While not attempting entry into tornadoes, they do penetrate regions of squall line and thunderstorm activity. In this way new knowledge is being gained about the structure, turbulence, and characteristics of these violent weather situations.

[3] In 1940 the Bureau was transferred from the Department of Agriculture to the Department of Commerce (where it has since remained), an indication of the increasing importance of weather to air commerce and transportation.

FIRST ROCKET SOUNDINGS

Of all the new technologies brought to the forefront by World War II and subsequently applied to weather observation, rocketry was certainly the most spectacular, if not the most significant. Actually, the concept of using rockets to sound the atmosphere had been proposed within the Weather Bureau as early as 1920. Based upon the preliminary work of Dr. Robert H. Goddard, father of American rocketry, the idea had been too far ahead of its time. Incapable of being implemented or tested, it was soon forgotten and had to await revival by subsequent events.

These events were provided by Nazi Germany's development and operational use of the A-4 bombardment rocket. More popularly known as the V-2, this 46-foot-long 14-ton missile was intended to strike at ground targets up to 200 miles away. En route it followed a flight trajectory that took it 55 miles above the earth. The performance and capabilities of the V-2 were unprecedented for any rocket vehicle. With it Germany had scored a genuine technological breakthrough.

The availability of captured V-2's, V-2 parts, and V-2 experts at the war's end provided the United States with the opportunity to use these vehicles for vertical soundings of the upper atmosphere. A series of scientifically instrumented V-2 firings began at the Army's White Sands Proving Ground in New Mexico during 1946 and continued into the fall of 1952. During this period about fifty V-2's were fired. Altitudes averaged slightly less than a hundred miles.

To replace the V-2 and to improve upon it, the American-designed Aerobee and Viking sounding rockets were developed.

For determining rocket attitude and orientation while in flight, also to reveal rates of spinning or tumbling, all three vehicle types were equipped with cameras. The pictures thus provided showed hundreds of thousands of square miles of the earth's surface and the clouds and cloud systems that lay above it.

Meteorologists were impressed by these photographs. They knew that the secret to understanding and forecasting the weather lay in observing as much of it as near-simultaneously as possible. The rocket's eye-view greatly increased their capability to do this (Fig. 5).

Fig. 5. Postwar firings of V-2, Aerobee, and Viking sounding rockets resulted in cloud cover pictures that laid the basis for satellite observations to
come. This is Viking 11, which climbed to a record height of 158 miles, May 24,
1954. (Official U.S. Navy photo.)

THE ARTIFICIAL SATELLITE IS BORN

Meteorologists were fascinated by the implications of routine rocket-borne photographic reconnaissance of the weather. At the same time, they had a feeling of frustration. Sounding vehicles of the V-2, Aerobee, and Viking class were too expensive and offered too brief a glimpse of the earth's cloud cover for routine observational use. What they wanted was a vehicle that would take pictures of the weather from rocket altitudes but that, unlike the rocket, would not immediately fall back to earth again. The more they talked about an observing vehicle that would stay up, the more they began to think about using artificial satellites.

Exactly who it was that first suggested the employment of orbiting spacecraft for meteorological observations is not known. Neither is it known when this application was initially proposed.

In 1951 Arthur C. Clarke, Chairman of the British Interplanetary Society, published a book containing a drawing that showed a meteorological satellite in polar orbit. That same year, a U.S. Air Force Project Rand report was issued carrying this title: *Inquiry into the Feasibility of Weather Reconnaissance from a Satellite Vehicle.* Drawing heavily upon the results of rocket-borne photography at White Sands, the document received only limited distribution because of its then classified nature.

Separately and about the same time, imaginative atmospheric scientists, like the Weather Bureau's late Dr. Harry Wexler, were becoming increasingly attracted to the unique suitability of satellites for studies, measurements, and analyses of the weather on a global basis. Although the achievement of orbital flight was still years away, Wexler and others pressed hard for the development of spacecraft for weather observations. His paper, *Observing the Weather from a Satellite Vehicle,* delivered at the Hayden Planetarium's Third Symposium on Space Travel (May 4, 1954, in New York) remains a classic in the field.

Efforts to gain support for satellite-based meteorology received a boost on October 5, 1954, when a Naval Research Laboratory Aerobee climbed about a hundred miles above White Sands to bring back the most meteorologically significant pictures yet obtained by a sounding rocket.

Centered over Del Rio, Texas, was a well-developed tropical storm. Its continued existence as such had not been detected by the conventional weather observing network in the area (Fig. 6).

Fig. 6. A composite of pictures taken by an Aerobee rocket from a height of a hundred miles over White Sands on October 5, 1954. In the upper left is the well-developed tropical storm accidentally discovered by this firing, a discovery that gave great impetus to meteorological observations from very high altitudes. (U.S. Weather Bureau photo.)

Examination of the pictures taken by the two 16 mm. cameras in the rocket's nose dramatically revealed the storm's continued presence in the area, together with its extent and its location. There could no longer be any doubt about the meteorological usefulness of pictures taken at rocket or satellite altitudes.

In 1955 the United States took its first official steps toward actually putting a satellite around the earth. An Army-Navy project, appropriately named Orbiter, was established early in the year. A few months later, it was superseded by another and different satellite program to be carried out under the direction of the Naval Research Laboratory as a U.S. contribution to the research activities of the International Geophysical Year. This program would be known as Vanguard.

During the next three years, efforts in rocketry and satellite circles were concentrated upon overcoming the technical problems and preparing the way for the first Vanguard launches. Somewhat overlooked in the excitement occasioned by the nation's first satellite hardware project was the development about then of a new rocket-type sounding device for wind-measuring observations.

To predict the drift and pattern of radioactive fallout resulting from nuclear testing, weathermen needed wind information at heights greater than the 50,000 to 100,000 feet normally attainable by sounding balloons. To obtain such information, they modified the Army's small antiaircraft Loki rocket. Depending upon its model designation, this Loki could climb to altitudes ranging from 100,000 to about 300,000 feet. At the peak of its trajectory, it woud eject lightweight "chaff," or radar-reflecting material. By using radar to track this material (tiny needle-like cylindrical dipoles of copper, brass, or aluminum) as it settled to the ground, an indication of wind direction and speed could be obtained. Other meteorological rocketsondes would also be developed. All essentially functioned on the same principle: (1) to reach a height above balloon altitudes and (2) to provide a slowly drifting and descending target, such as chaff, a metallized parachute, or an air-inflated balloon, for tracking by electronic means (Fig. 7).

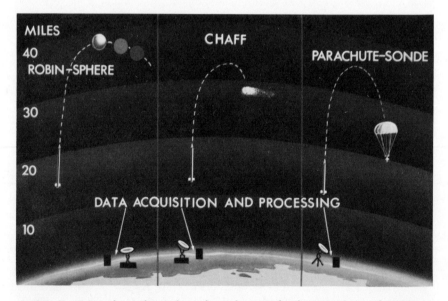

Fig. 7. From the Loki rocket, there has evolved since the mid-1950's a family of meteorological rocketsondes that utilize electronic tracking of their slowly earthward-drifting payloads to determine the direction and speed of the winds. (NASA photo.)

In view of the long-standing interest expressed in using satellites for weather observations, it is not surprising that meteorological experiments were among those selected for inclusion in Vanguard.

The first attempt to orbit such an experiment took place on September 26, 1958, with Vanguard Satellite Launching Vehicle #3. Inside this three-stage rocket was a small 20-inch diameter sphere, the satellite package. Inside that were various items of equipment including two photocells. These would scan the earth's surface, sense the brighter illumination of sunlit clouds, and report their observations to the ground via radio. The launching of Vanguard SLV #3 was not successful.

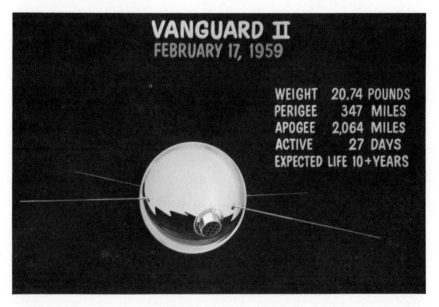

Fig. 8. Vanguard II, first United States satellite to carry a meteorological experiment into orbit. (NASA photo.)

Another Vanguard was scheduled for February 17, 1959 (Fig. 8). A similar photocell experiment was on board. This time orbit was achieved. But the satellite's spin, which was to have provided the scanning motion for the cells, proved erratic. Little in the way of useful cloud observations resulted from Vanguard II.

The next try at satellite-borne cloud mapping was made with a television system adapted from one used on an earlier lunar probe vehicle. Explorer VI, boosted by a Thor-Able, carried this system into orbit August 7, 1959. Pictures were obtained and transmitted to earth, but their quality was unsatisfactory (Fig. 9).

Fig. 9. A television system aboard Explorer VI attempted mapping of the earth's cloud cover but with marginal success. (NASA photo.)

The fourth in this series of early orbital meteorological experiments attempted something different. Instead of looking at cloud cover, this was designed to obtain information on the earth's heat budget. As the term "budget" implies, its instrumentation was to measure input and outgo of radiant energy.

The amount of solar energy received daily by the earth varies greatly over the surface of the globe. Obviously, the tropics receive more sunlight than does the Arctic or Antarctic. Radiation from the sun is not only unevenly distributed, it is unevenly absorbed and reflected by the earth as well. Much of it is reflected back into space. A small percentage is absorbed by the atmosphere. And roughly

40 per cent has been calculated to be absorbed by the earth's surface which then radiates in longer wavelengths as heat.

The worldwide intensity and distribution of this (1) incoming, (2) reflected, (3) absorbed, and (4) re-emitted energy is not well known. Yet this unequal distribution of energy and the thermal imbalance that it inevitably creates are important factors that "drive the atmosphere."

To put it another way, the earth's blanket of air is like a giant heat engine that derives its power through energy received from the sun. Weather is partially the result of the shifting and changing of the atmosphere as it tries to adjust to the unequal distribution of heat within it.

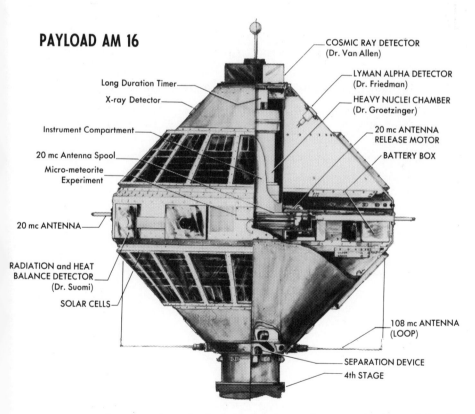

PAYLOAD AM 16

COSMIC RAY DETECTOR (Dr. Van Allen)
LYMAN ALPHA DETECTOR (Dr. Friedman)
HEAVY NUCLEI CHAMBER (Dr. Groetzinger)
20 mc ANTENNA RELEASE MOTOR
BATTERY BOX
108 mc ANTENNA (LOOP)
SEPARATION DEVICE
4th STAGE
Long Duration Timer
X-ray Detector
Instrument Compartment
20 mc Antenna Spool
Micro-meteorite Experiment
20 mc ANTENNA
RADIATION and HEAT BALANCE DETECTOR (Dr. Suomi)
SOLAR CELLS

Fig. 10. The Suomi heat budget experiment is shown in the lower left of this drawing of scientific equipment carried by Explorer VII. (NASA photo.)

To measure the earth's energy influx and outgo, an experiment was designed by Professor Verner E. Suomi of the University of Wisconsin and flown aboard Explorer VII on October 13, 1959 (Fig. 10). The satellite carried hemispheres of different sensitivities to (1) direct or reflected solar radiation and (2) the longer-wave radiation emitted by the earth. In this way, both types of radiation could be observed and their intensities compared while the spacecraft overflew continents, oceans, and varying latitudes.

Up to this point, meteorological experiments had been orbited as parts of and incidental to other more extensive scientific satellite programs, namely Vanguard and Explorer. There existed as yet no spacecraft that could be identified specifically as meteorological in nature or purpose. One, however, was in the making.

In early 1958, a program was established within the Defense Department's Advanced Research Projects Agency to develop a spacecraft for meteorological purposes. It would be called TIROS, an acronym standing for Television Infrared Observation Satellite.

On April 13, 1959, responsibility for TIROS was transferred to the National Aeronautics and Space Administration (NASA), which had meanwhile come into existence. One year later, April 1, 1960, the first of this family of weather satellites was launched from Cape Canaveral (now Cape Kennedy).

With its entry into orbit, a whole new chapter of meteorology was begun.

II

The Coming of Age

A Picture Chronicle of TIROS
and Nimbus

TIROS

At 6:40 A.M. on April 1, 1960, a Thor-Able rocket thundered from its Cape Canaveral launch pad. Climbing upward and outward in a northeasterly direction, it placed a 270-pound, hatbox-shaped spacecraft into orbit 450 miles above the earth. TIROS I, the world's first meteorological satellite, had been born (Fig. 11).

TIROS I was launched at an angle of 48 degrees to the equator. As it circled the earth once every ninety-nine minutes at 17,000 mph, the satellite ranged from 48° North to 48° South. The Point of Verticality (shown over Saudi Arabia, Fig. 12) is the predicted position at which its cameras would look straight down at the earth following injection into orbit.

Because TIROS I was spin-stabilized, its two television cameras could view the earth straight down only at certain times. Spinning at 8 to 12 rpm, the satellite acted as a gyroscope, seeking to maintain a fixed attitude in space. Its cameras variously looked directly at, glancingly at, or completely away from the earth's surface (Fig. 13).

TIROS II, launched November 23, 1960, was equipped with a magnetic coil intended to provide some control over its orientation in space (Fig. 14). With this technique, it was found possible to alter satellite attitude by as much as 15 degrees a day. The coil has been an integral part of TIROS design ever since (Fig. 15).

23

Fig. 11. The launching of TIROS I. (NASA photo.)

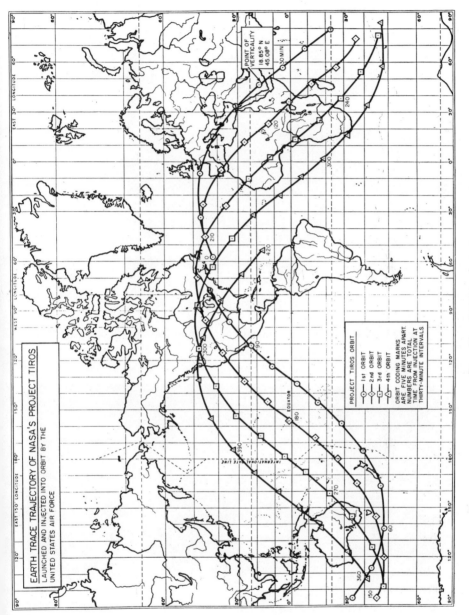

Fig. 12. (NASA photo.)

25

Fig. 13. The dashed lines indicate the approximate north and south limits of TIROS I's picture coverage. (NASA photo.)

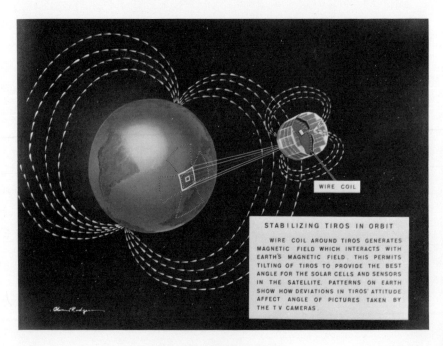

Fig. 14. (NASA photo.)

Fig. 15. Inside a spherical cage that simulates the magnetic field of the earth, a TIROS undergoes tests of its magnetic attitude control system. (NASA photo.)

Infrared Observations—Type I. By viewing the earth and its atmosphere at selected wavelengths in the infrared, different types of information can be obtained. Observations made in the 5.5- to 6.5-micron region (a micron is one millionth of a meter) will sense the radiant energy at the top of the layer of water vapor absorption (No. 1, Fig. 16). The 8- to 12-micron region of the spectrum is the so-called "water vapor window." At these wavelengths, a satellite-borne radiation sensor can "see" all the way down to the earth's surface unless clouds block the way. If they do, then it "sees" the cloud tops instead (No. 2). The energy emitted by these clouds is an indication of their temperature, and the temperature is an indication of their height. Solar radiation reflected by the earth and its atmosphere can be measured in the range of 0.2 to 5.0 microns (No. 3), while a sensor operating at 7 to 30 microns will obtain an approximation of the total radiation emitted by the earth itself and its atmosphere (No. 4).

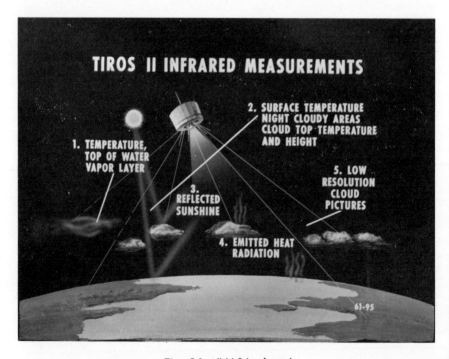

Fig. 16. (NASA photo.)

While TIROS I carried only television cameras, TIROS II was equipped with radiation sensors as well. Some of these were combined in a radiometer, an instrument that (1) looked out of the

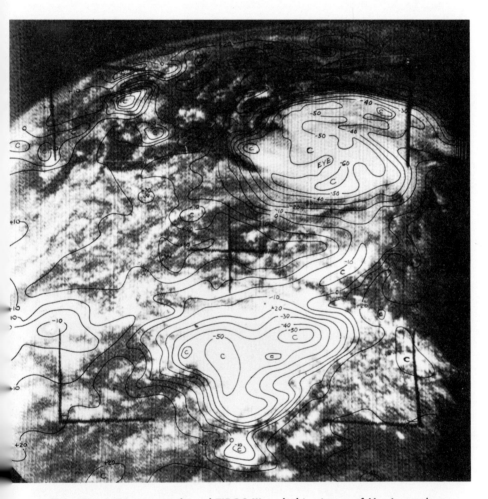

Fig. 17. A TV camera aboard TIROS III took this picture of Hurricane Anna (upper right) near 13° North, 72° West. Its radiometer also viewed the region in the 8- to 12-micron band of the infrared spectrum. At these wavelengths, it observed the thermal radiation of the earth's comparatively warm surface and of the colder cloud tops. Note the correspondence between what the camera saw and what the radiometer sensed. This striking analysis was made by Professor T. Fujita of the University of Chicago. The temperatures cited, in degrees Centigrade, are approximate values. (U.S. Weather Bureau photo.)

spacecraft at 45 degrees to the spin axis and (2) scanned the earth by making use of the satellite's spinning motion and its movement along the orbital path. Four of these sensors operated at the wavelengths indicated above. A fifth one was sensitive in the 0.55- to 0.75-micron band (the visual part of the spectrum). It obtained low resolution cloud pictures (No. 5) that were intended for use in TIROS infrared experimentation as a gross reference check.

Infrared Observations—Type II. To learn more about how our planet (1) receives radiation from the sun, (2) reflects it back into space, (3) absorbs it, and (4) then re-emits energy appropriate to its temperature, TIROS II carried a second radiation experiment. Designed by V. E. Suomi as a follow-on to his experiment aboard Explorer VII (see p. 22), it consisted of radiation sensors mounted on two telescoping arms extending out from the spacecraft's sides. At the end of each arm was a detector consisting of a black hemisphere and a white hemisphere mounted against a mirror surface. The black element was sensitive to (1) the visible radiation emitted by the sun and reflected by the earth and its atmosphere and (2) the longer-wave, earth-emitted radiation. The white

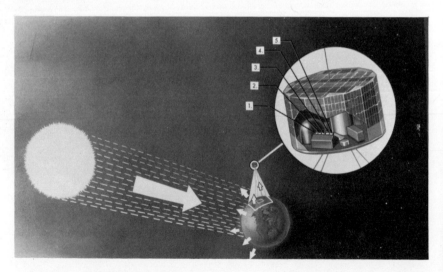

Fig. 18. Although this artist's conception does not show the arms or sensors of the Suomi experiment, it depicts some of the radiative processes involved. The numbers refer to the five-channel radiometer also on board. Radiation sensors have been variously carried by TIROS II, III, IV, and VII. (NASA photo.)

element, on the other hand, reflected (1) and absorbed (2). The readings of these differently sensitive bolometers were then compared (Fig. 18).

Infrared Observations—Type III. Another type of radiation experiment flown aboard TIROS consisted of two cones, one containing a black and the other a white detector. Operating on the same differentiating principle as the Suomi experiment, these elements looked down upon the earth from the satellite baseplate, viewing the same areas as did the television cameras (Fig. 19).

With the addition of infrared sensors, TIROS began to live up to its name—*T*elevision *I*nfrared *O*bservation Satellite. Figure 20 shows the fourth in the series atop a pedestal awaiting a weight and balance check. Its TV cameras protrude like giant eyes from the baseplate. To generate power for the cameras, sensors, and associated equipment, more than 9,000 solar cells (1 × 2 centimeters) cover the spacecraft's top and sides. At the extreme right can be seen the mirror-mounted white hemisphere of a Suomi radiation experiment.

Maintaining the TIROS Spin. When TIROS separates from the Delta third stage, it is spinning at about 120 rpm. To slow it to the desired rate of 12 rpm, two weights attached to cables wrapped around the spacecraft are permitted, via a timer, to unwind and "de-spin" the satellite. The weights drop off when they have completely unwound.

The minimum spin rate at which TIROS can keep stable in orbit is 8 rpm. As the spin slows and this minimum is approached, a pair of small solid-fuel rockets, mounted on the rim of the baseplate, are fired by radio command from the ground. There are ten of these rockets (five pairs) mounted on each TIROS. They can be used only once. Firing of a pair increases the spin rate by about 3 rpm.

A typical Delta vehicle (Fig. 26) used for TIROS launches measured about 90 feet in length and weighed about 57 tons. Its first-stage liquid-propellant engine generated about 170,000 pounds of thrust during its 2½-minute burn time. The second stage, a 7,500-pound-thrust motor, also liquid propellant in nature, fired for about 160 seconds. The solid-fueled top stage engine operated about 40 seconds and produced approximately 3,000 pounds of thrust.

Fig. 19. In this photo of TIROS subsystems and components, the two small cones are near the center of the table. In the immediate foreground are two TV cameras and, in between, a magnetic tape recorder. (NASA photo.)

Fig. 20. (NASA photo.)

Fig. 21. TIROS satellites are eighteen-sided polygons that measure 22½ inches high and 42 inches in diameter, and weigh between 270 and 300 pounds. This one has just been mated to its Thor-Delta launch vehicle at Cape Canaveral, now Cape Kennedy. (NASA photo.)

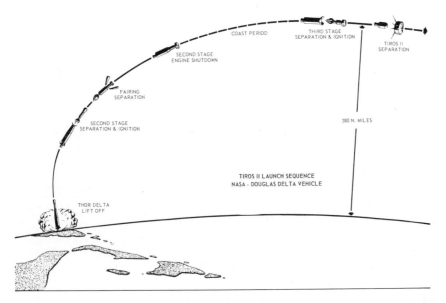

COAST PERIOD

THIRD STAGE
SEPARATION & IGNITION

TIROS II
SEPARATION

SECOND STAGE
ENGINE SHUTDOWN

FAIRING
SEPARATION

SECOND STAGE
SEPARATION & IGNITION

380 N. MILES

TIROS II LAUNCH SEQUENCE
NASA - DOUGLAS DELTA VEHICLE

THOR DELTA
LIFT OFF

Fig. 22. TIROS I was orbited for NASA by the U.S. Air Force with a Thor-Able vehicle. Subsequent launchings have been NASA-conducted using Thor-Delta rockets and generally resembling this operational sequence. (NASA photo.)

Fig. 23. Complex Number 17 at Cape Kennedy where TIROS-carrying Thor-Deltas are launched. (NASA photo.)

Fig. 24. Thor-Delta being erected in the gantry preparatory to a TIROS launch. (NASA photo.)

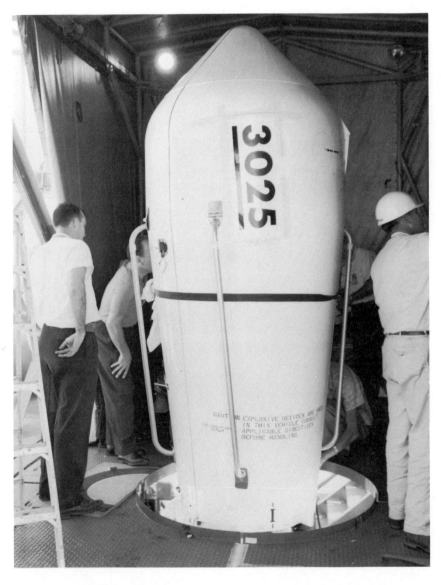

Fig. 25. TIROS V "buttoned up" and ready for launch. This bulbous nose fairing will protect it during its ride up through the atmosphere into the emptiness of space. (NASA photo.)

Fig. 26. A TIROS launch at night. (NASA photo.)

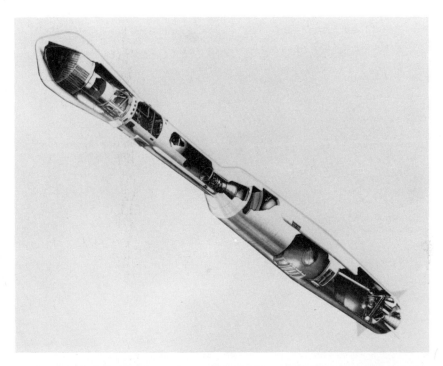

Fig. 27. Artist's sketch of a representative Thor-Delta launch vehicle showing major design features. The bottom or first stage consists primarily of tankage to hold the liquid oxygen and hydrocarbon fuel that propel the DM-21 Thor. The connection of this stage to the next is covered by a transition skirt that narrows the diameter to that of the AJ10-118 above it. This unit, too, contains tankage for its nitric acid oxidizer and its hydrazine fuel. Between the second and third stages is an equipment compartment. Here is located the radio guidance system that insures accuracy of flight during first and second stage burning. At the top is the third stage, a solid propellant X248-type rocket, to which is mounted the satellite payload. (NASA photo.)

TIROS design was fairly well standardized early in the program's history (Fig. 28). Solar cells convert sun rays into electrical energy, which is stored in nickel-cadmium batteries. Power from these batteries operates the television cameras, the infrared equipment, the magnetic tape units that record the TV and IR data for playback to the ground, and the transmitters and beacons. Radio transmissions from the satellite are made with four antennas spaced 90 degrees apart at the baseplate. The satellite receives its commands via another antenna on its top. TIROS I and II carried nar-

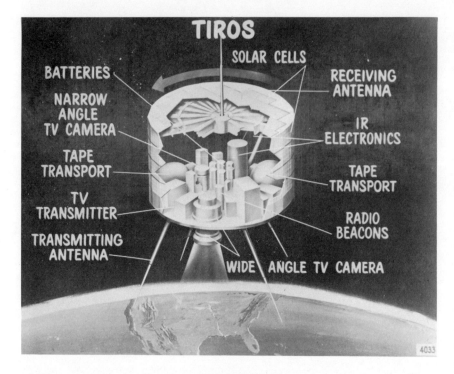

Fig. 28. (NASA photo.)

row and wide-angle lens TV cameras, but succeeding ones have used various lens combinations. The radio beacons serve a dual purpose: (1) to provide tracking signals and (2) to transmit telemetry-type information on the condition and state of operation of the spacecraft itself.

How Picture-taking Is Commanded. TIROS is commanded by three ground stations located at Wallops Island, Virginia, Point Mugu, California, and Fairbanks, Alaska. These CDA (Command and Data Acquisition) stations give two basic commands: (1) to take pictures in a remote area or within sight of the station itself and (2) to transmit these pictures to the ground.

The Weather Bureau, through its National Weather Satellite Center at Suitland, Maryland, decides which region along the orbit is of the greatest meteorological interest. NASA's TIROS Technical Control Center, located at the Goddard Space Flight Center, Greenbelt, Maryland, computes the command signals that must be sent to the satellite if it is to provide the coverage desired. These signals are then passed to one of the CDA stations, which transmits them to TIROS as it passes overhead.

Aboard the satellite, these signals actuate a clock that triggers the TV camera when the desired geographical region has been reached. The camera snaps one picture every thirty seconds until thirty-two pictures—the capacity of the magnetic tape recorder—have been taken. There are two cameras and two tape recorders. A total of sixty-four pictures can therefore be obtained during each orbit. Cameras can be operated simultaneously or independently of one another.

When the spacecraft returns to within radio range (about 1,500 miles), the station commands it to transmit the pictures it has stored. If the station is in daylight and the satellite is so oriented that its cameras face the earth, it may also order TIROS to take and transmit direct pictures of the area. Direct pictures are taken at ten- or thirty-second intervals, while taped ones are always spaced thirty seconds apart.

Following readout, the CDA facility will command and set the clock for the next orbit.

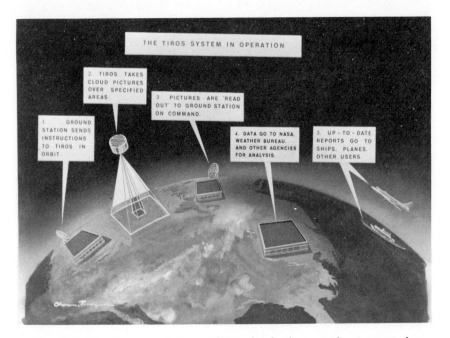

Fig. 29. Visualization of how TIROS cloud photography is carried out. (NASA photo.)

Fig. 30. NASA's TIROS Technical Control Center. (NASA photo.)

Fig. 31. Command and Data Acquisition (CDA) station at Wallops Island, Virginia. The large antenna on the left is a multielement high-gain array that receives TIROS TV picture readout. Immediately to its right is a smaller antenna, also multielement, over which beacon and beacon-transmitted information is received. (NASA photo.)

Fig. 32. Here is one of the two 85-foot diameter antennas erected at Gilmore Creek, near Fairbanks, Alaska, for commanding and acquiring data from present and future meteorological satellites. One "dish" belongs to NASA, the other to the Weather Bureau. The Point Mugu CDA antenna, located on San Nicolas Island off the California coast, is also of the parabolic reflector type. It is smaller, however, its diameter being 60 feet. (NASA photo.)

Fig. 33. The NASA Gilmore Creek (Fairbanks) Command and Data Acquisition station and antenna. (NASA and U.S. Weather Bureau photo.)

Fig. 34. With this assemblage of equipment at Gilmore Creek, TIROS is commanded and its television, infrared, and telemetry signals received, recorded, and displayed. (NASA and U.S. Weather Bureau photo.)

The value of satellite photography for large-scale weather observations was dramatically demonstrated by TIROS I within hours after launch. Television pictures taken during its first weeks of operation (Fig. 35) enabled meteorologists to see the weather over (a) the Red Sea, (b) the Gulf of Aden, and (c) the Indian Ocean as no man had ever seen it before.

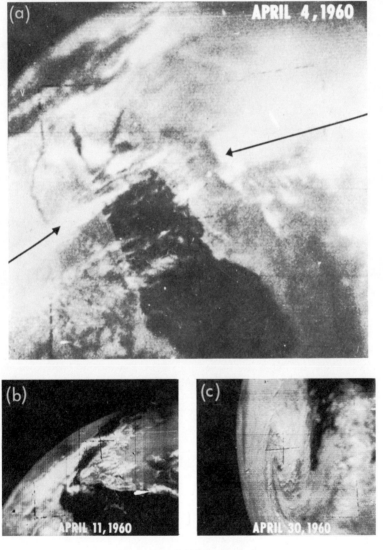

Fig. 35. (NASA photos.)
Arrows indicate jet stream clouds (*left*) and mountain clouds (*right*).

Fig. 36. Perhaps the most famous weather satellite picture ever taken—the "square cloud" photographed by TIROS I close to the Oklahoma-Texas border on May 2, 1960. Within a few hours, it enlarged and spread northward, bringing hailstorms and tornadoes into central Oklahoma. (U.S. Weather Bureau photo.)

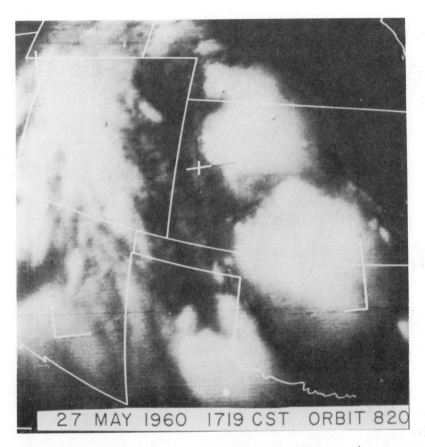

27 MAY 1960   1719 CST   ORBIT 820

Fig. 37. As a result of experience gained with TIROS, weathermen pay special attention to satellite photos showing bright clouds that are isolated and have fairly well-defined edges. These three, bright in contrast to and separated from the cloud field to the west, were dropping hailstones as big as baseballs when this picture was taken. Shortly afterward, the southernmost spawned a tornado. Pictures like this can greatly assist in pinpointing and giving warning of severe local storms *if* they can be processed in time and their information relayed fast enough to the affected areas. Analysts have added state boundaries to this picture to indicate the geographical locations involved. (U.S. Weather Bureau photo.)

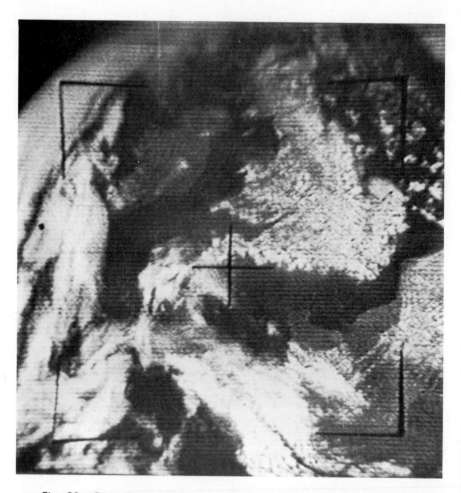

Fig. 38. Great Britain, Ireland, and the French and Belgian coasts are seen in this TIROS IV picture, taken at 1:20 p.m., local London time, on April 14, 1962. England and Scotland stand out as a result of a heavy cover of cumulus clouds. Ireland, in contrast, is hardly visible. Its cloudiness is little developed and it basks in the sunshine of the spring day. (U.S. Weather Bureau photo.)

actual size

Fig. 39a. In TIROS a vidicon tube this small can take a picture of a weather system this big:

Fig. 39b. More than 600,000 square miles of ocean weather are in this view of a North Atlantic vortex. (U.S. Weather Bureau photo.)

Each image is retained long enough by the vidicon to be scanned and electronically converted into a TV-type signal for recording on magnetic tape or for direct transmission. Readout of each 400-foot tape (one per camera) requires one and a half minutes and automatically rewinds it for the ensuing orbit. Playback is in reverse, the last picture taken being the first read out.

The ability of TIROS to overfly great expanses of oceanic weather has enabled it to spot and give warning of otherwise undetected severe tropical storms (Fig. 40). As "hurricane hunters" in the Atlantic and "typhoon hunters" in the far Pacific, TIROS spacecraft

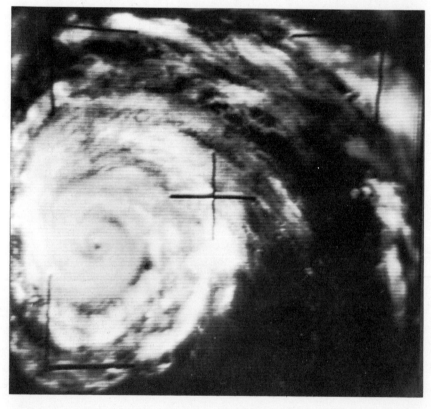

Fig. 40. TIROS V took this picture of Typhoon Ruth on August 18, 1962, about 300 miles south-southeast of Tokyo. Winds were 125 knots at the time. The storm's "eye" can be seen in the lower left-hand corner. (U.S. Weather Bureau photo.)

Fig. 41. This curious cloud pattern was photographed by TIROS V at about 7° South, 92° West. An inversion, in which the temperature increases rather than decreases with altitude, sits over this oceanic area. Like a giant, invisible cap, it inhibits convection and prevents the development of these clouds into more mature and conventional-appearing formations. (U.S. Weather Bureau photo.)

play an important role in finding the position and tracking the movement of these powerful and dangerous disturbances.

If there are no clouds, the TIROS camera sees the earth's surface instead. When there is a minimum of haze and industrial smoke and when surface features contrast sufficiently, unusual pictures often result (Figs. 42 through 46).

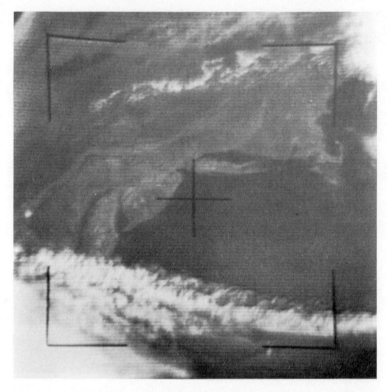

Fig. 42. Outlined within the black L-shaped and +-shaped fiducial or reference marks superimposed upon TIROS pictures by the camera stretches the eastern seaboard of the United States. (U.S. Weather Bureau photo.)

Fig. 43. From the nominal 450-mile height of most TIROS satellites, the camera looks down to photograph the Nile River and Delta, the Red and Mediterranean Seas, and the Suez Canal. The black line marking the course of the Nile is not the river itself, but the vegetation growing along its banks. (U.S. Weather Bureau photo.)

Fig. 44. The eastern end of the Mediterranean, showing Cyprus, the Sinai Peninsula, and the Holy Land. The elongated dark spot to the right of the center fiducial mark is the Dead Sea. (U.S. Weather Bureau photo.)

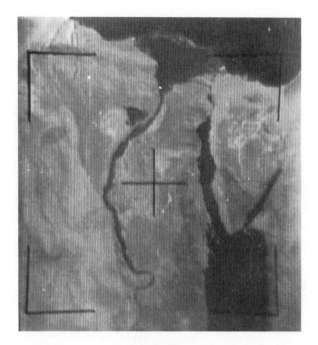

Fig. 43

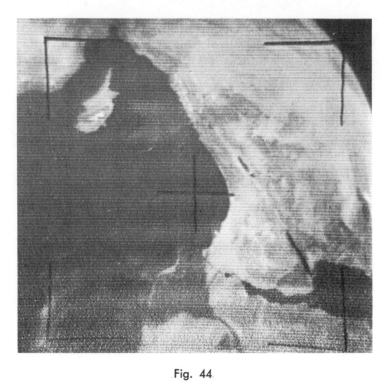

Fig. 44

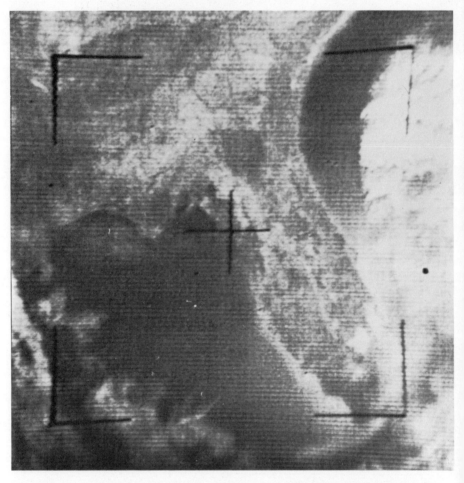

Fig. 45. The Florida Peninsula, Georgia, and South Carolina as seen by TIROS IV. The offshore clouds above the Atlantic delineate the Gulf Stream edge. Interesting, too, is the sun's reflection off Lake Okeechobee. (U.S. Weather Bureau photo.)

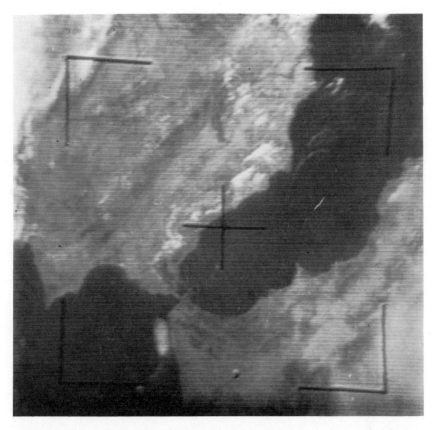

Fig. 46. Portugual, Spain, the Strait of Gibraltar, and North Africa are clearly visible in this picture taken in bright sunlight over where the Mediterranean meets the Atlantic. Like home television images, TIROS TV pictures consist of scan or raster lines—500 in number. (U.S. Weather Bureau photo.)

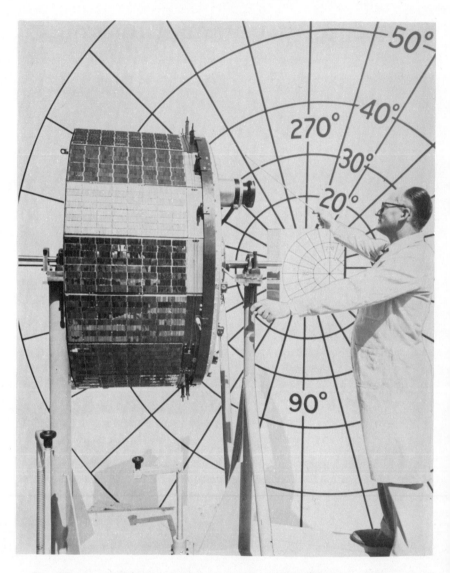

Fig. 47. Successful picture-taking requires careful calibration of the camera system. Here the cameras of TIROS II, one with a wide-angle lens of 104°, the other with a narrow-angle lens of 12°, are being checked for focus and field of view. (NASA photo.)

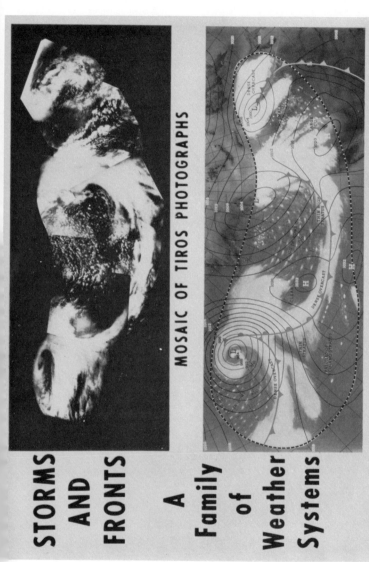

STORMS AND FRONTS

A Family of Weather Systems

MOSAIC OF TIROS PHOTOGRAPHS

WEATHER MAP, MAY 20, 1960, WITH TIROS CLOUD DATA

Fig. 48. From individual pictures, meteorologists can piece together mosaics that provide a composite view of the weather as it exists in a wide swath thousands of miles long. Here are compared (1) a mosaic of cloud pictures ranging from the Great Lakes on the right to the Northern Pacific Ocean on the left and (2) the weather map for the same day. Their close correlation substantiates the saying: "Nature uses clouds to draw her own weather maps." (NASA and U.S. Weather Bureau photo.)

57

Picture Analysis and Information Distribution. Upon readout to the
Command and Data Acquisition station, TIROS pictures are recorded on magnetic tape from which they are displayed on a TV
tube. This tube is photographed and a 35 mm. film strip, containing
the pictures just received, is produced. Prints are quickly obtained
and on them are drawn latitude and longitude lines that have been
previously computer-produced using predicted orbital position and
attitude information.

Based upon these pictures, Weather Bureau personnel at the
station prepare a cloud map—they call it a *nephanalysis*—that graphi-
cally represents the picture content. This "neph" and selected individual pictures are sent by land-line facsimile to the Bureau's National
Weather Satellite Center. There, at Suitland, the cloud information
is incorporated into operational analyses, charts, and forecasts.

From Suitland, these maps and pictures are then retransmitted
by land-line facsimile to weather stations in the United States or
beamed by radio overseas. So that foreign countries without facsimile receiving equipment might nevertheless have the benefit of
TIROS observations, the "nephs" are also coded and sent globally
via teletype and radio (Fig. 49).

Weather information is among the world's most perishable. For
this reason, every effort is made to have the TIROS data out of Suitland and on its way to meteorological users as soon as possible. As
a rule, these data are in user hands within three hours following
satellite readout.

Satellite meteorologists, as weathermen who work with TIROS
data are often called, plot their nephanalyses or cloud charts on two
basic map projections. One is the *polar stereographic,* which places
the North or South Pole in the center of the projection. In Fig. 50,
"nephs" have been prepared on a polar stereographic for the Southern Hemisphere. Similar maps are drawn for the Northern. Because
this type projection becomes severely distorted in the equatorial regions, the *Mercator projection* is used in low latitudes (Fig. 51).

Facsimile. Nephanalyses and cloud pictures are sent from the
readout stations to Suitland and from Suitland to the meteorological
community by facsimile.

Facsimile is a communications technique by which pictorial matter is transmitted from one place to another. On the sending end,
the material is line-scanned by a beam of light that is reflected onto

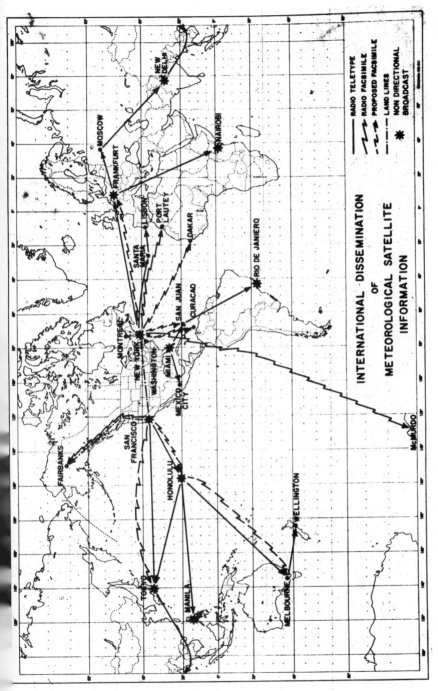

Fig. 49. The radio facsimile broadcasts shown in this chart as "proposed" are currently in operation except for the San Francisco-to-Tokyo and the New York-to-Dakar links. (U.S. Weather Bureau photo.)

59

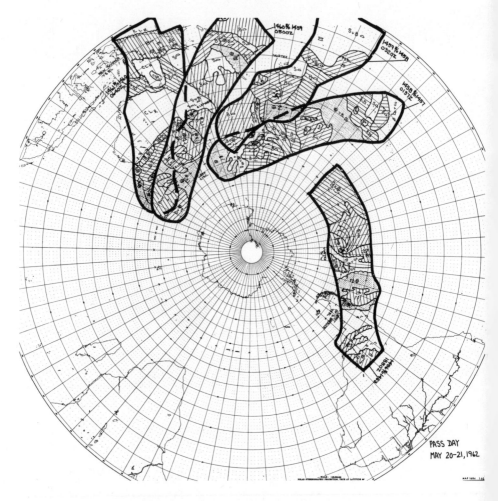

Fig. 50. (U.S. Weather Bureau photo.)

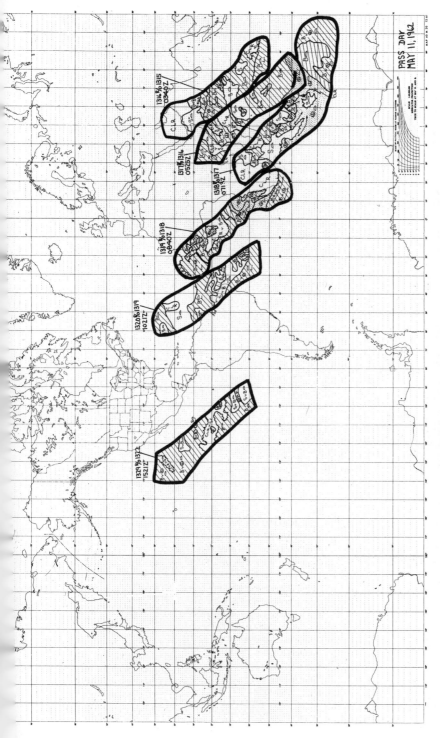

Fig. 51. The legend "1329 R/O 1322, 1521Z" on the westernmost nephanalysis indicates that the sequence of pictures was taken at 3:21 p.m., Greenwich Mean Time, during Orbit 1322. Readout took place seven passes later. (U.S. Weather Bureau photo.)

61

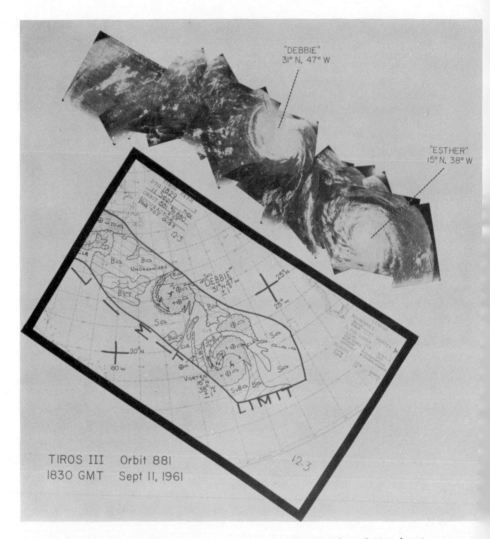

Fig. 52. A picture mosaic—with accompanying nephanalysis—showing two hurricanes, Debbie and Esther, about 1,500 miles apart. The latter was discovered by TIROS III two days before conventional observations would probably have revealed her existence. (U.S. Weather Bureau photo.)

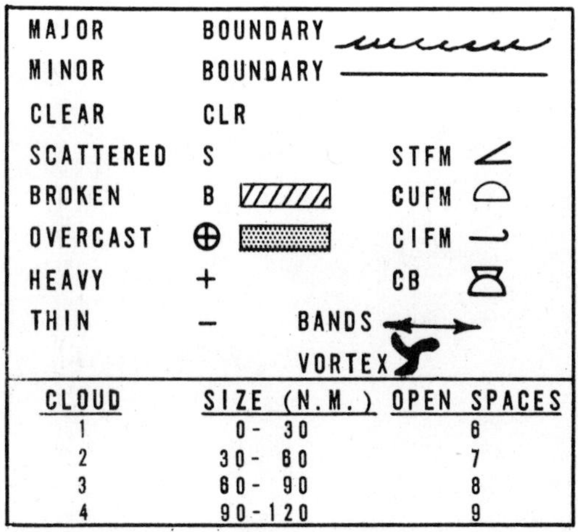

MAJOR	BOUNDARY		
MINOR	BOUNDARY		
CLEAR	CLR		
SCATTERED	S	STFM	∠
BROKEN	B ▨	CUFM	⌂
OVERCAST	⊕ ▦	CIFM	⌣
HEAVY	+	CB	ප
THIN	−	BANDS	
		VORTEX	

CLOUD	SIZE (N.M.)	OPEN SPACES
1	0- 30	6
2	30- 60	7
3	60- 90	8
4	90-120	9

Fig. 53. Symbols for the preparation of nephanalysis. STFM, CUFM, CIFM, and CB stand for stratiform, cumuliform, cirriform, and cumulonimbus type clouds. Early in 1964 these symbols were added to and expanded upon to make the informational content of the "nephs" more meaningful. (U.S. Weather Bureau photo.)

or otherwise sensed by a photoelectric cell. This converts light intensity into electric current. Differences in shading will produce differences in intensity and, therefore, in current. Thus, the scanning operation results in an electrical output whose fluctuations correspond to the blackness, whiteness, or grayness of the image being sent.

At the receiving end, this varying current is passed through special paper that reacts to leave a mark—the stronger the current, the darker the mark—as it, too, is scanned line by line. In this way the original image is reconstituted.

In another version, the facsimile receiver uses its fluctuating electrical input to activate a light that scans photosensitive paper with a brightness proportional to the current strength. This is the basis for *photofacsimile*.

Picture Archival. From the magnetic tape recordings made by ground stations during TIROS picture readout, high-quality transparencies are produced. These 35 mm. films—"positives" for viewing or "negatives" for making opaque prints—are stored chronologically on 100-foot reels that researchers can order at nominal cost from

Fig. 54. These are facsimile machines at the Wallops Island Command and Data Acquisition station. Nephanalyses are transmitted over the large conventional "fax" machines to the right. In the left corner is the "photofax" over which individual TIROS pictures are also processed. (NASA photo.)

the Weather Bureau's National Weather Records Center, Asheville, North Carolina.

The picture content of each archival reel is listed in catalog form. In these catalogs, the pictures are described in terms of (1) reel number, (2) orbital pass number, (3) mode of transmission—taped or direct, (4) camera number—#1 or #2, (5) identity of ground station that received the picture, (6) month and day picture was taken, (7) hour and minute—expressed in Greenwich time—of the middle frame of the picture sequence, (8) time interval—in seconds—between the individual frames, (9) the number of usable frames in the sequence, (10) the geographical area covered, and (11) the presence or absence of identifying landmarks and distinctive cloud features.

When a TIROS satellite ends its useful operating life, a complete catalog of its pictures is published by the Superintendent of Documents. Price varies according to the number of pictures taken and, therefore, the catalog size (Fig. 55). While a TIROS is still operating, preliminary summaries of its cloud photography are periodically published and issued by the National Weather Satellite Center (Fig. 56).

When snow fields appear in satellite pictures, they often look like clouds. Usually they can readily be identified because, unlike clouds, they show little change and no movement. Snow falling in the mountains blankets the slopes and heights in white. Valleys, however, may be snow-free or in shadow, giving the area a veined appearance (Figs. 58, 59, and 60). Accurate knowledge of snow cover is important to hydrologists and others concerned with predicting and controlling "run-off" from spring thaws. Eventually, satellite instruments may be developed that will reveal the depth, compactness, and water content of snow fields as effectively as cameras can define their geographical extent.

Automatic Picture Transmission (APT). TIROS VIII, launched December 21, 1963, carried a revolutionary new television camera system into orbit. Unlike previous TIROS cameras, this one had no tape recorder. It read out its picture to the ground as soon as it was taken and then proceeded to take and transmit another.

Called the Automatic Picture Transmission (APT) system, this technique of direct readout utilized a 1-inch so-called "sticky vidicon" that retained its image for 200 seconds. During this period, its 800-line picture was slowly scanned line-by-line and simultaneously transmitted to earth where it was received and then reconstituted on a facsimile recorder. Following that, the overall 208-second prepare, expose, develop, and readout cycle would be repeated.

A timer aboard TIROS VIII programmed the APT system to operate for about thirty minutes maximum during each orbit. Picture transmission required no interrogation from the ground. Readout could be achieved by *any* station within signal range and equipped with the necessary antenna, receiver, and facsimile machine.

This first APT-equipped TIROS also carried a conventional half-inch vidicon that took and read out pictures upon command in the customary tape-recorded or direct "in sight of the station" transmission modes.

U. S. DEPARTMENT OF COMMERCE
LUTHER H. HODGES, Secretary
WEATHER BUREAU
F. W. REICHELDERFER, Chief

KEY TO METEOROLOGICAL RECORDS DOCUMENTATION NO. 5.34

CATALOGUE OF METEOROLOGICAL SATELLITE DATA—TIROS IV TELEVISION CLOUD PHOTOGRAPHY

WASHINGTON, D. C. : 1963

Fig. 55.

UNITED STATES DEPARTMENT OF COMMERCE
WEATHER BUREAU

CATALOGUE OF

TIROS VII And VIII

CLOUD PHOTOGRAPHY

FOR

DEC. 1963; JAN. And FEB. 1964

TIROS VII   (Passes 2437 thru 3777)
TIROS VIII (Passes 0004 thru 1023)

NATIONAL WEATHER SATELLITE CENTER

Washington, D. C.

May 1964

Fig. 56.

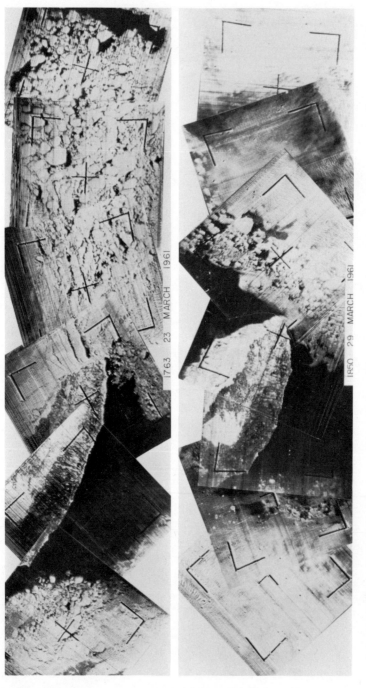

1763   23 MARCH 1961

1850   29 MARCH 1961

Fig. 57. These mosaics, made from photographs taken over the Gulf of St. Lawrence by the narrow-angle camera of TIROS II during orbits 1763 and 1850 give striking proof that satellites can perform valuable ice as well as weather surveillance. Each photo in these mosaics comprises an area about 75 miles square. Resolution of surface detail is about 0.2 to 0.6 of a mile. Note how readily the satellite has observed the breakaway of the ice from Anticosti Island, also how clearly visible are the larger leads and floes. With these pictures TIROS demonstrated immense potential for providing information operationally and economically important to ships seeking to navigate ice-blocked waters. (U.S.

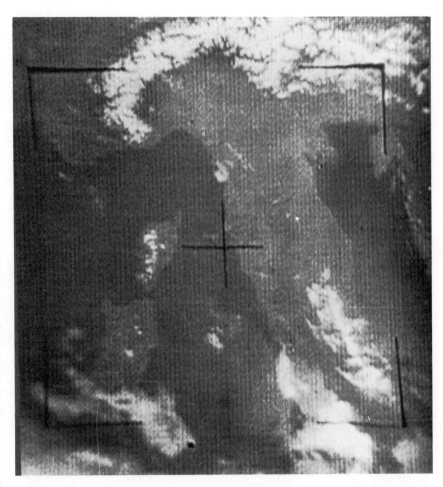

Fig. 58. A TIROS picture of the snow-covered Alps. (U.S. Weather Bureau photo.)

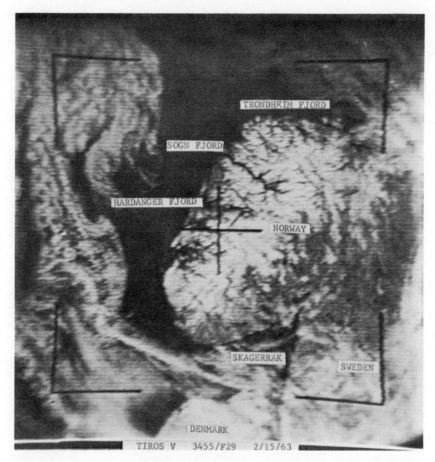

Fig. 59. The winter-draped mountainous and fjord-indented terrain of Scandinavia. (U.S. Weather Bureau photo.)

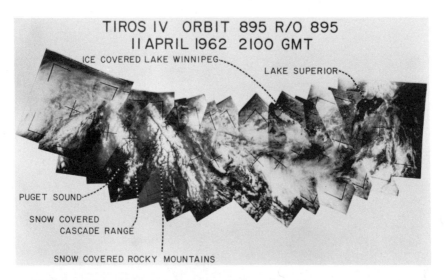

TIROS IV ORBIT 895 R/O 895
II APRIL 1962 2100 GMT

ICE COVERED LAKE WINNIPEG

LAKE SUPERIOR

PUGET SOUND

SNOW COVERED
CASCADE RANGE

SNOW COVERED ROCKY MOUNTAINS

Fig. 60. This mosaic shows (1) the difference in the appearance of snow fields in mountainous and comparatively flat terrain and (2) the ability of satellite cameras to survey the extent of snow cover. (U.S. Weather Bureau photo.)

Fig. 61. APT pictures are received via this eight-turn, helical, 14-foot-long antenna. This one is located on the roof of the Weather Bureau's National Weather Satellite Center, Suitland, Maryland. (U.S. Weather Bureau photo.)

71

Fig. 62. APT ground station console (*left*) and facsimile recorder (*right*).
To place these stations within the economic reach of foreign countries, equipment emphasis has been upon simplicity, and costs have been held to a minimum. (U.S. Weather Bureau photo.)

Fig. 63. An APT picture of the United States Pacific Coast shows considerable cloud cover detail. It should be remembered that this is a facsimile recording made by reconstituting the APT camera image, one line at a time, on 8-inch-wide electrosensitive paper at a rate of 240 scan lines per minute. (U.S. Weather Bureau photo.)

Fig. 64. The APT camera takes a picture about 800 miles square when pointed straight down at the earth from TIROS altitudes. (NASA photo.)

More than forty APT ground stations have been built and distributed for worldwide test and evaluation. The locations of some are shown in Fig. 65. APT enables "real time weather pictures" to be obtained when an APT satellite passes within range of an appropriately equipped ground station. Information conveyed in this manner will be particularly useful in isolated areas where meteorological communication networks are scarce, unreliable, or nonexistent.

Summary of TIROS Operations. For a summary of TIROS operations, see table on page 76.

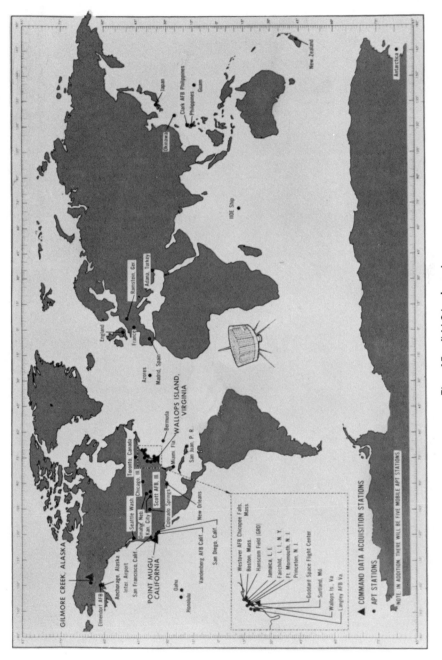

GILMORE CREEK, ALASKA

Elmendorf AFB
Anchorage, Alaska
Inter. Airport
San Francisco, Calif.

POINT MUGU,
CALIFORNIA

Oahu
Honolulu

Vandenberg AFB Calif.
San Diego, Calif.

Seattle, Wash.
Omaha, Neb.
Kan. City
Chicago, Ill.
Scott AFB, Ill.
Colorado Springs
New Orleans

Toronto, Canada

Bermuda
Miami, Fla.
San Juan, P. R.

WALLOPS ISLAND,
VIRGINIA

England
France
Azores
Madrid, Spain

Ramstein, Ger.
Adana, Turkey

HOE Ship

Okinawa

Japan
Clark AFB, Philippines
Philippines
Guam

New Zealand

Antarctica

Westover AFB Chicopee Falls,
Mass.
Boston, Mass.
Hanscom Field (GRO)
Jamaica, L. I.
Fairchild, L. I. N.Y.
Ft. Monmouth, N. J.
Princeton, N. J.
Goddard Space Flight Center
Suitland, Md.
Wallops Is. Va.
Langley AFB Va.

▲ COMMAND DATA ACQUISITION STATIONS

● APT STATIONS

NOTE: IN ADDITION THERE WILL BE FIVE MOBILE APT STATIONS

Fig. 65. (NASA photo.)

75

SUMMARY OF TIROS OPERATIONS
as of March 31, 1964
(Orbital data are nominal)

TIROS	I	II	III	IV	V	VI	VII	VIII
Launch date	4/1/60	11/23/60	7/12/61	2/8/62	6/19/62	9/18/62	6/19/63	12/21/63
Days operational	79	69	108	125	320	388	Still operating	Still operating
Orbital inclination	48°	48°	48°	48°	58°	58°	58°	58°
Apogee (statute miles)	460	450	500	530	600	440	400	460
Perigee (statute miles)	430	380	460	440	360	420	380	430
Orbital period (minutes)	99	98	100	100	100.5	98.7	97	99
Camera #1	12°	12°	104°	104°	104°	104°	104°	104°
Camera #2	104°	104°	104°	76°	76°	76°	104°	APT
Meteorologically usable pictures	19,389	25,574	24,000	23,370	48,547	59,830	54,391	15,691

NOTES:

(1) IR experiments were carried on II, III, IV, and VII but not operationally used.

(2) Beginning with TIROS V, orbital inclination was increased to 58°. Depending on orientation, cameras can "see" about 12° farther, extending photo coverage to roughly 70°.

(3) Command and Data Acquisition stations for TIROS I were at Kaena Point, Hawaii, and Fort Monmouth, New Jersey; for II at Point Mugu, California, and Fort Monmouth; thereafter at Point Mugu and Wallops Island, Virginia. In September, 1963, a third station began operation at Fairbanks, Alaska.

NIMBUS

Even before the first TIROS had flown, plans were underway for an eventual successor—Nimbus.

For Nimbus there was evolved a spacecraft design consisting of three major elements: (1) a *sensory ring,* (2) a *stabilization and control system,* and (3) a *solar array.*

The sensory ring, 13 inches deep and 57 inches in diameter, mounts the TV cameras, IR equipment, batteries, and related communications and electronics systems.

Above the ring and connected to it by a truss sits the stabilization and control system housing. This is a hexagonal box containing sensors to detect deviations in attitude and pneumatic jets and flywheels to compensate for them.

Two paddles, 39 × 96 inches each, make up the solar array. These are attached to a shaft running through the stabilization and control system housing. Solar cells, 2 × 2 centimeters and numbering 10,000, are arranged on one side of the paddles. They rotate in flight to keep this "face" pointed toward the sun.

Total weight of the first Nimbus spacecraft was about 800 pounds; overall width, 134 inches; height, 114 inches.

To achieve the global coverage that TIROS could not provide, Nimbus was designed for polar orbit and earth orientation (Fig. 67).

Orbital altitude for Nimbus "A," first of the series, was to be about 500 nautical (575 statute) miles. The orbit was to be inclined about 80° to the equator and be sun-synchronous. A sun-synchronous orbit is one in which the orbital plane precesses or moves about the earth at a rate equivalent to the earth's own movement around the sun (360° in a year, or slightly less than 1° per day). If Nimbus was launched to cross the equator at local noon (and correspondingly at local midnight on the other side of the globe), sun synchronism would guarantee that it would generally maintain this timetable throughout its operating life. This means (1) that observations would be made at a constant time of day and (2) that the solar paddles need be turned along only one axis since the plane of the orbit would always contain the sun-earth line.

Earth orientation is achieved by stabilizing Nimbus in pitch, roll, and yaw. Two horizon sensors, one viewing forward along the orbital path and the other backward, provide information on pitch

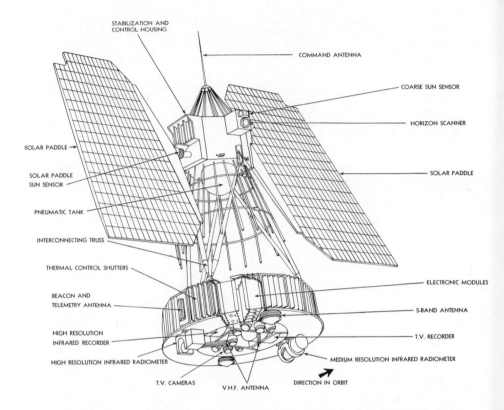

Fig. 66. Most Nimbus features shown here are self-explanatory or have been previously identified. The *solar paddle sun sensor* controls the positioning of the paddles with respect to the sun. The spherical *pneumatic tank* contains nitrogen gas to actuate the attitude-correcting pneumatic jets (not shown) on the top and sides of the control system housing. The *thermal control shutters* serve to maintain temperature within the sensory ring at 25° C., plus or minus 10°, by opening and closing to provide radiant cooling as required. The *V.H.F.* (Very High Frequency) *antenna* transmits the pictures taken by the APT camera while the *S-band antenna* provides the readout communication link for the TV pictures and High Resolution Infrared (HRIR) data. The *Medium Resolution Infrared radiometer* was not carried aboard the initial Nimbus flight. (NASA photo.)

Fig. 67. (NASA photo.)

and roll error. Yaw is sensed by a sun sensor during the initial stages of stabilization and by a gyro thereafter.

Plans called for the first Nimbus to be orbited by a two-stage Thor-Agena B (Fig. 68). To enable the spacecraft to fit within the Agena nose, it would be carried aloft with solar paddles folded. It would be launched from PMR (Pacific Missile Range) where geography safely permits southbound firing into polar trajectories. Launch would be at midnight to achieve the desired midnight-and-noon orbit. After the first-stage Thor burned out and dropped away, the Agena would ignite. Explosive bolts and springs would jettison the Nimbus protective shroud. After a brief "first burn," the Agena would coast about fifty minutes until it attained a 500-nautical-mile altitude. Then it would reignite and use its "second burn" to achieve the required orbital speed. As it did, the spacecraft would be separated from it at about 4 feet per second, using springs for impulse. (Fig. 69). Shortly thereafter, the Agena would be yawed away and,

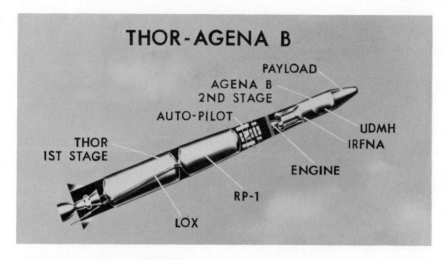

Fig. 68. In the nomenclature accompanying this sketch, LOX stands for liquid oxygen, RP-1 for Rocket Propellant-1 (a form of hydrocarbon fuel), IRFNA for Inhibited Red Fuming Nitric Acid, and UDMH for Unsymmetrical Dimethyl Hydrazine. (NASA photo.)

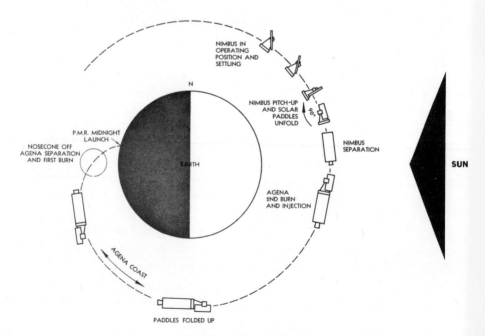

Fig. 69. (NASA photo.)

with a retrorocket, slowed and started on its way back to the earth's atmosphere. Upon spacecraft separation, a programmer would unfold the solar paddles and command a 90° pitch-up. At this point, Nimbus would achieve its earth orientation and, assisted by the pneumatic jets and flywheels of its stabilization system, start its global circumnavigation under positive attitude control.

Fig. 70. Full-scale model of Nimbus, without solar cells, being placed in environmental chamber for testing under simulated space conditions. (NASA photo.)

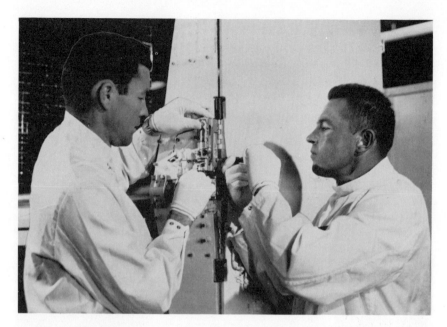

Fig. 71. Installation of one of the electric motors that unfolds the Nimbus solar paddles during injection into orbit. (NASA photo.)

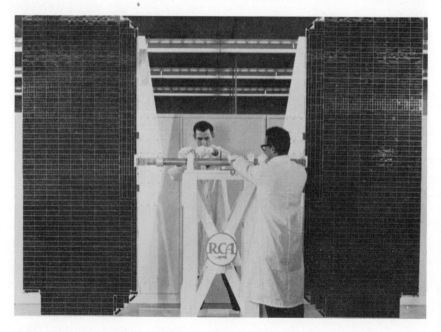

Fig. 72. The Nimbus paddles mounted on the shaft that rotate to keep the solar cells oriented toward the sun. (NASA photo.)

Nimbus "A" was launched August 28, 1964, at 12:57 A.M. Pacific
Daylight Time. Its Command and Data Acquisition stations were
85-foot-antenna-equipped NASA facilities at Gilmore Creek, Fairbanks, Alaska, and Rosman, North Carolina. It achieved an 81.3°
elliptical retrograde orbit with an apogee of 579 statute miles and a
perigee of 263. Orbital period amounted to 98.3 minutes. The success of this spacecraft can be best described by some of the pictures
that it took (Figs. 73–75).

The remarkable quality and scientific value of the observations
made by the Automatic Picture Transmission (APT) and Advanced
Vidicon Camera System (AVCS) of Nimbus "A" and particularly by
its high resolution infrared radiometer leave no doubt about this
vehicle's future impact upon satellite meteorology and upon meteorological satellites.

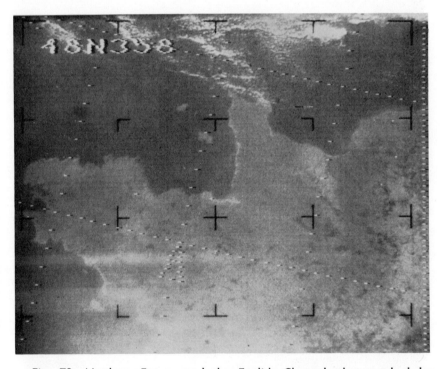

Fig. 73. Northern France and the English Channel photographed by
Nimbus "A" from a height of 460 statute miles. The white dots are computer-
produced grid lines of latitude and longitude. The computer has also printed
out the position (see upper left) of the intersection marked by the north-pointing
arrow near the center. An AVCS camera took this picture. (NASA photo.)

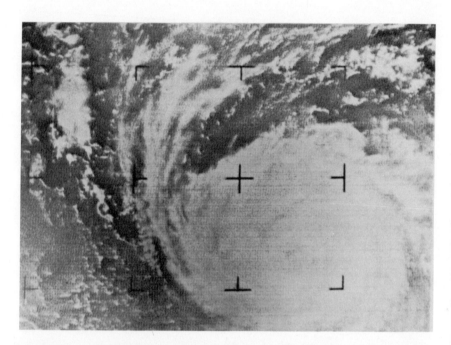

Fig. 74. Hurricane Dora captured by the Nimbus APT camera. (NASA photo.)

Nimbus Camera System. Whereas the conventional TIROS carried two half-inch vidicon cameras, Nimbus "A" had three 1-inch vidicons.

These AVCS (Advanced Vidicon Camera System) units were positioned in the base of the sensory ring so that one looked straight down and the others to its right and left at an angle of 35 degrees. Each had a 37-degree field of view.

It was intended that all three cameras could take a picture simultaneously about every ninety-one seconds. The resulting picture triad would encompass about 400 nautical miles in a north-south direction and 1,500 miles from east to west. Some thirty-two pictures could thus be taken by each camera during the daylight portion of the orbit. They would be stored on a single recorder using a four-track magnetic tape (three tracks for video information, one for timing). Recorder storage capacity was sixty-four pictures per camera (two orbits). Readout would be commanded by the CDA station when the spacecraft approached within communicating range.

Nimbus camera exposure time was forty milliseconds (forty thousandths of a second). The iris was variable and set by the orientation of the solar paddles with respect to the sun. A precision reticle pattern, similar to the fiducial marks on TIROS photographs, was etched on the vidicon face for reference purposes. To record the Nimbus pictures, 1,200 feet of half-inch magnetic tape (erased at time of readout) were used. As with TIROS, the tape recorder could be bypassed upon command and pictures obtained by direct transmission. AVCS picture resolution would be about ½ mile.

In addition to the three-camera AVCS system, an Automatic Picture Transmission (APT) camera would be carried. APT and its associated ground equipment have been previously described.

The AVCS picture contained about 800 scan or raster lines.

Fig. 75. Another view of Hurricane Dora, this time viewed *at night* (1:27 a.m., Eastern Daylight Time) by the Nimbus high resolution infrared system. Careful examination of this picture will also reveal as a gray background the land mass of the eastern United States. Florida, Georgia, and the Carolinas are obscured by the hurricane, but to the upper right are visible the characteristic shapes of Chesapeake and Delaware Bays. The ability, here demonstrated, to take cloud pictures at night represents a major technological and scientific achievement. (NASA photo.)

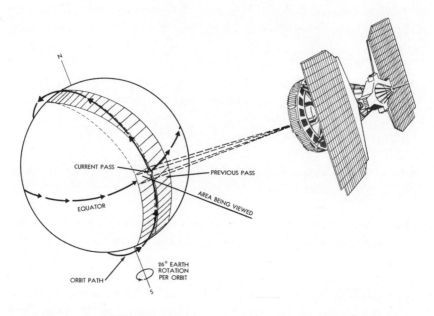

Fig. 76. Nimbus, its paddles oriented to face the sun directly behind it, is seen crossing and photographing the equatorial zone. At this point, its pictures taken during two sequential orbits are just about contiguous. As the satellite moves toward the poles, however, the earth tapers and picture coverage increasingly overlaps. (NASA photo.)

Nimbus Infrared Observations.   Because cloud cover requires adequate illumination to be photographed, TV cameras cannot be used at night. A different observing technique must be employed. This involves infrared sensing and was achieved on Nimbus "A" by a radiometer that rotated and scanned the earth's surface in strips or swaths at right angles to, that is, across the satellite's path.

The energy sensed by this radiometer represented areas of high and low emission. This information, in turn, could be translated into areas of relative warmth and cold. Nighttime clouds are generally colder than the surface, except possibly when the surface is ice- or snow-covered. Regions of relative cold, sensed by the radiometer and recorded on magnetic tape, are therefore regions of cloud cover.

On the ground following readout, the thermal energy sensed by the satellite was played back scan line by scan line on a recording that recomposed the energy-emission "picture" as it was seen by the

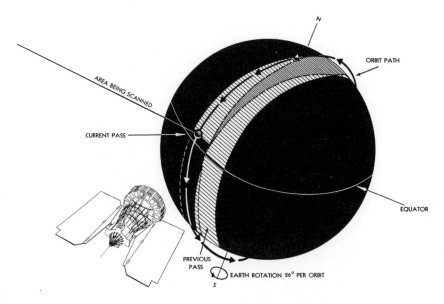

Fig. 77. Using an infrared radiometer, Nimbus scans the dark side of the
earth. (NASA photo.)

radiometer. The High Resolution Infrared Radiometer aboard the
first Nimbus operated in the 3.4 to 4.2 micron region of the spectrum,
another so-called "water vapor window" (see p. 28). The resolution
was about 5 miles.

III

The Years Ahead

Initiation of an operational system for globally observing the earth's cloud cover on a daily, continuing, and routine basis; expansion of weather satellite observing capabilities; use of weather satellites for non-meteorological applications; collection and distribution of weather information; growth and development of meteorological spacecraft technology to make possible these new capabilities and applications; training of weathermen as astronauts and their assignment aboard orbiting space platforms; and increased international understanding and goodwill—in these terms the future of satellite meteorology will be written.

AN OPERATIONAL SYSTEM

As of November 1, 1964, eight TIROS spacecraft had been successfully orbited out of eight attempts. This spectacular record of launch success has been matched by an equally impressive history of useful observations. Each TIROS has provided many thousands of television pictures, the informational content of which has been applied by the Weather Bureau to the improvement of its analyses and forecasts.

This operational application of weather satellite information was begun with TIROS I within hours following launch. During that spacecraft's operating life of seventy-nine days, some 19,000 meteorologically useful pictures were obtained. The TV observations of the seven succeeding TIROS have been utilized in a similar manner. Infrared data obtained by TIROS radiometers have thus far been put to research rather than operational uses.

All eight TIROS spacecraft and the Nimbus are research-type

vehicles funded for, developed, and flown by NASA to explore the applicability of space technology to atmospheric observation and investigation.

Those operational benefits that have resulted from TIROS have come as by-products. Under a cooperative arrangement, NASA makes immediately available to the Weather Bureau the TV photos as they are received at the Command and Data Acquisition stations. NASA also programs TIROS picture-taking in accordance with Weather Bureau requests.

Early in the TIROS program, it was recognized that these operational benefits were important enough to be treated as prime objectives rather than by-products. In October, 1960, representatives of the Weather Bureau, NASA, the Federal Aviation Agency, and the Department of Defense decided that plans should be prepared for the establishment of a national operational weather satellite system.

An interagency group, called the Panel on Operational Meteorological Satellites, was formed two months later. In April, 1961, it submitted its recommendations. Briefly stated, the most significant were:

1. The United States should undertake to develop a National Operational Meteorological Satellite System (NOMSS) "at the earliest possible date."
2. Management responsibility for NOMSS should be assigned to the U.S. Weather Bureau.
3. Development and procurement of spacecraft, launch vehicles, and ground support equipment should be provided by NASA as should also the services of launch, tracking, and, as required, command and data acquisition.
4. The operational system should evolve from the NASA research and development program, initially making use of Nimbus, then under development.
5. The TIROS program should be extended to continue an operational capability pending the flight availability of Nimbus.

Selection of Nimbus as the basis for NOMSS was dictated by the promise that this polar-orbiting and earth-stabilized vehicle held for twice-daily coverage of the entire surface of the earth. By contrast, a TIROS was fortunate to observe 15 to 25 per cent of the earth in any twenty-four-hour period.

Support for the Panel's plan came from the President's Science

Advisory Committee later that same month. On May 25, 1961, in a message to Congress outlining important national needs, President Kennedy asked for an appropriation to the Weather Bureau that would "help give us at the earliest possible time a satellite system for worldwide weather observation." On September 30 he signed Public Law 87-332, which appropriated $48 million to the Bureau for this purpose.

To fulfill its managerial responsibilities for this operational system, the Weather Bureau (1) established the National Weather Satellite Center (NWSC) adjacent to its National Meteorological Center in Federal Office Building #4, Suitland, Maryland, and (2) entered into a formal agreement with NASA covering the system's implementation.

The NASA TIROS program was extended as had been recommended, and its operational products continued to be utilized by the Weather Bureau. Recognizing that NASA, a research agency, should not be constrained or limited unduly by the operational usage to which its research and development TIROS was being put, Weather Bureau funds were set aside to procure up to three conventionally configured TIROS. These would be used to supplement the operational coverage incidentally being provided by NASA's research and development vehicles. They would also enable NASA to proceed with new and different TIROS experiments— new cameras and sensor systems, new orbits, and new altitudes, for example—without degrading or jeopardizing the interim-like operational system that had gradually evolved.

It was to the Nimbus, meanwhile, that the meteorological community was looking for the true operational system.

Nimbus, however, was experiencing developmental problems. A technically advanced vehicle, its design contained features, of which the stabilization and attitude control system was one, that had never been flown on a spacecraft before. Like many a previous technically advanced program, and like many to come, Nimbus encountered engineering difficulties and its schedule began to slip.

While Nimbus completion and launch were being delayed, techniques began to appear that offered alternative ways of doing some of the things with other satellites that had once been thought possible or practicable only with Nimbus.

An examination of these alternatives and of the relative costs involved led to a reorientation of the operational system planning in January, 1964. Instead of being based upon Nimbus, the National Operational Meteorological Satellite System would, for the first few years at least, utilize TIROS technology and TIROS itself in a modified form.

This first phase of the reoriented operational program is called the TOS (*TIROS Operational Satellite*) System. Its spacecraft will be a TIROS in a so-called "cartwheel" configuration, with cameras looking out from the rim instead of from the baseplate as was the case in TIROS I through VIII.

In size, shape, or weight, the TIROS wheel will differ little from its predecessors. It will spin at about 10 rpm as they did. But its spin orientation will be substantially different. By means of magnetic torquing (see page 23), the spin axis will be oriented so that the satellite is aligned with its orbital track and rolls "like a wheel" along it (Fig. 75). Horizon sensors will trigger the cameras so that they will take their pictures when pointed straight down.

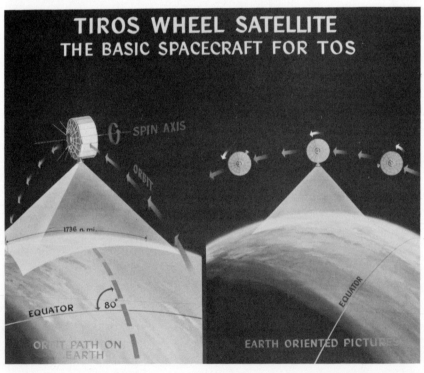

Fig. 78. Artist's conception of the *TIROS Operational Satellite* (TOS) in flight. The picture swath width (1,736 nautical miles) and orbital inclination (80° retrograde) are approximations. (U.S. Weather Bureau photo.)

Two versions of TOS will be flown at first: one equipped with two Automatic Picture Transmission (APT) cameras for direct readout, the other equipped with two Nimbus-type 1-inch AVCS vidicon cameras and tape recorders for on-board storage of pictures and command readout. Having two cameras on each spacecraft will provide redundancy and longer spacecraft operating lifetimes. It is planned to have one APT version and one AVCS version operational in orbit at all times beginning in late 1965. Eventually, the APT and AVCS camera systems may be combined and only one TOS spacecraft version employed.

Developed and launched by NASA for the Weather Bureau, these TOS vehicles will be placed 750 nautical miles above the earth in near-polar sun-synchronous orbits. At this altitude, their period will amount to 113 minutes per orbit. Each satellite will circle the earth 12.7 times a day. Equator crossings will take place at mid-morning or mid-afternoon. Launch will be from Cape Kennedy (Atlantic Missile Range) or Vandenberg Air Force Base (Pacific Missile Range) using an improved Thor-Delta or a Thor-Able-Star vehicle.[1]

As a prelude to these operational launches, two experimental TIROS "wheels" were to be orbited in late 1964 and again toward mid-1965 to test and demonstrate the system. Implementation of the operational phase will be accompanied by a continuing program intended to extend the observing capability and, therefore, the meteorological usefulness of the TOS system. This future capability will most likely include nighttime cloud cover and heat balance observations.

TOS readout will be performed by means of the Weather Bureau-owned 85-foot parabolic antenna at Gilmore Creek, Fairbanks, Alaska, and from a second similarly equipped Command and Data Acquisition site at Wallops Island, Virginia.

The technical problems in instituting an operational weather-observing satellite system are unfortunately too often oversimplified. Popular conceptions notwithstanding, there is more to it than altitude, orbit, and vertically pointing cameras with a wide field of view.

There are these factors to be considered, for instance:

1. Resolution, that feature of the system that will decide the meteorologist's ability to discriminate between clouds or other elements.

[1] The Atlantic Missile Range is being redesignated as the Eastern Test Range (ETR); the Pacific Missile Range as the Western Test Range (WTR).

2. Camera viewing angle that, if it is too oblique, will distort or even completely obscure picture details.
3. Picture contiguity, which is essential if completely global camera coverage is to be obtained.
4. Frequency of observation, which will determine how many satellites have to be put in orbit and, once there, have to be replaced in order to maintain an operating system.
5. Frequency of readout, reflecting the extent to which the weather data user is (a) insistent upon having his information available to him after each orbit or (b) is willing to wait the time involved in having the spacecraft collect and store two or three orbits before reading it out to CDA stations for processing, analysis, and distribution.

Many other factors are also involved but are too specialized to be gone into here. Perhaps it is adequate to say that an operational weather satellite system is based upon a very large number of (1) meteorological, (2) scientific, (3) engineering, and (4) economic "trade-offs"—all of them complex and all of them interrelated.

In combination they determine (1) the spacecraft characteristics; (2) its camera systems and other sensors; (3) the orbital altitude, period, and inclination; (4) the lifetimes and numbers of satellites required; and (5) the numbers and locations of the ground stations. In defining the parameters for such a system, the requirement for Automatic Picture Transmission (APT) must be taken into account, as must the need for nighttime cloud information.

EXPANSION OF OBSERVING CAPABILITIES

Meteorologists have insatiable appetites for observation-type information. The nature of their work, which is both a science and an art, demands it.

This appetite for data has led some to look impatiently for the application of weather satellites to other than cloud-mapping missions.

One member of the international meteorological community recently described the situation in the following way:

Thanks to NASA and TIROS, we've been able to obtain well over a quarter-of-a-million TV pictures of the earth. Operationally we've used these pictures to detect, locate, and follow the development of major storms or other particularly significant weather occurrences. Our researchers have learned a lot from them too . . . about the extent, movement, and characteristics of weather systems, about severe local storms, and about the correlation of cloud types (as observed by satellites) with existing weather conditions at the surface.

The IR or infrared observations have been helpful in making available new information on the earth's heat budget. They've been useful, too, in laying the groundwork for the employment of IR, aboard Nimbus, for example, to provide cloud cover information at night.

Cloud information is useful, but it is only one small piece in the meteorological jigsaw puzzle. Satellite pictures don't tell us what's going on inside the clouds or below them. We don't know whether there is precipitation, how severe, or of what type. We can only guess unless we have related information from other type observations, what sorts of winds or turbulence are to be found with them.

To be sure, experienced weathermen can deduce from cloud appearances the types of weather and weather conditions that probably exist in the region photographed. What we need is not deductions and educated guesswork. We want observations, direct observations of these conditions and phenomena. We want, whenever and wherever possible, quantitative data.

Such data are not easily come by when the weather is overflown at a distance of hundreds of miles. The requirement for this information and the technological difficulties in acquiring it unite to present a substantial challenge to those who build and those who use satellite vehicles for meteorological purposes. It is a challenge being met.

An infrared spectrometer is under development that is expected to look down from its orbital path and be able to provide temperature profile information for the atmosphere below.

The potential of using sferics detectors is being studied. Sferics, short for "atmospherics," is the term used for the electrical discharges found naturally in weather. Because these discharges in the form of lightning are indicative of the presence of thunderstorms, the possibility of detecting them from a satellite offers promise of identifying and locating such storms within dense or widespread cloud cover.

Satellite-borne radar has been carefully looked at as a means to obtain information on precipitation falling from clouds. Thus far, analysis of the potential of this type of radar application has failed to excite much enthusiasm among either satellite technologists or weathermen.

Both, however, are looking at the possibilities of using satellite-carried microwave radiometers (those sensitive in the microwave or, more popularly, the radar frequency part of the electromagnetic spectrum) as supplements to the existing television cameras and infrared sensors.

It is when it comes to sensing wind direction and speed that the problem of quantitative observations might appear most severe. If clouds are present, it may be possible, sometime in the future, to track them photographically and derive wind information from them.

But suppose there are no clouds. Then another type of wind "tracer" in the form of constant-level balloons will possibly be used. The concept for so doing has been known for some years and by various names. The most descriptive is GHOST (Global Horizontal Sounding Technique). And appropriate too—floating in a random distribution at various heights within the atmosphere, these balloons will have to be as evanescent as ghosts if struck by aircraft or in-gested by jet engines.

The practicability of using satellites to take a positional "fix" on GHOST-type tracer balloons is currently under study for possible incorporation of the concept into the operational system.

As currently visualized, this would involve the launching of hun-dreds of plastic film balloons, so designed that they would seek and maintain a constant level or altitude. By being inflated to a super-pressure, these cells would undergo expansion and contraction of the gas without changing in volume.

Each balloon would be fabricated and equipped to respond ac-tively or passively to interrogation signals received from passing satellites. Their replies would be recorded by the spacecraft, stored, and read out to CDA stations. Data processing techniques would extract balloon position information from these interrogations and responses—as many as three each might be possible from each bal-loon during a single orbital pass. By entering this constantly up-dated position information into a running plot of balloon trajectories and locations, balloon flight paths could be reconstructed and averaged-out wind force and direction obtained.

The 500-millibar [2] height, or about 18,500 feet, is of particular

---

[2] A millibar is a unit measurement of atmospheric pressure. In weather circles, it has largely replaced the older and more commonly known expression of pressure in terms of inches of mercury.

interest to meteorologists and represents a key level in computer-produced analyses of the state of the atmosphere. The first GHOST balloons might be expected, therefore, to be placed and distributed at this altitude.

If they are to be, however, a number of questions must first be answered satisfactorily:

1. How can these balloons best be launched—from what locations and using what techniques—in order to achieve a satisfactory distribution?
2. Initially, how far should each be spaced from the others?
3. Once launched, what will their trajectories be?
4. How quickly, how severely, and from what causes will their distribution pattern be disrupted?
5. What will be the effect upon them of a major storm development?
6. Will they congregate in "graveyard areas" and be trapped there by air that is stagnant or going no place in particular? (One such area is suspected to exist southwest of California.)
7. Is there an exchange of air across the equator so that balloons launched in the Southern Hemisphere might cross over into the Northern and vice versa?
8. How often will these GHOST balloons have to be replaced in order to maintain an adequate network?
9. What duration should these balloons be capable of and should they contain provisions to terminate their flight? If so, how soon, for what reason, and with what techniques?
10. How accurately can a satellite obtain a position "fix" on a drifting GHOST balloon—using what optimum technique?
11. What type of electronic equipment and circuitry must such a balloon carry if it has to receive and respond to a satellite's signal?
12. Using thin film and other examples of the latest electronic techniques, can the solar cells, batteries, circuits, antenna, and receiver/transmitter elements be made lightweight, low density, and frangible enough so that they could be struck by a high-speed aircraft or swallowed by a jet engine without hazard to the plane or to those aboard?
13. By distributing the mass of the electronics as much as possible over the surface of the balloon, can the damage-by-collision danger to aircraft be kept within limits tolerable to the Federal Aviation Agency, the Air Line Pilots Association, and the flying public?

14. How much will this highly sophisticated electronic approach cost per balloon?
15. And, finally, how many balloons will be needed annually for each level of the atmosphere for which wind information is desired?

Upon the answers to these difficult questions, the decision will be made to adopt or not to adopt GHOST as a subsystem of NOMSS. It is a decision that will be made (1) partly on the basis of meteorological usefulness; (2) partly, perhaps primarily, on the basis of aviation safety considerations; (3) partly on economic or cost-effectiveness grounds; and (4) partly on international political considerations, since it will involve the continuing and frequent overflight of foreign countries.

In the years to come, new technologies, too, will be developed that will have application for weather-observing by satellites. Where appropriate, these new techniques will most certainly be placed aboard spacecraft to improve man's capability to keep the restless atmosphere under effective meteorological surveillance.

NON-METEOROLOGICAL APPLICATIONS

The usefulness and value of weather satellites are not limited to their meteorological observations. Their camera systems, sensors, and wide-ranging global coverage enable them, actually and potentially, to perform a variety of non-meteorological tasks.

Many of these tasks—the detection of forest fires, the tracking of locust clouds, and the observation of volcanoes, for example—are not the responsibility of the Weather Bureau or of NASA. Why, then, undertake them with weather satellites? Because the departments and government organizations that are responsible for them have no satellite programs of their own. In the national interest, their requirements should be met as much as possible by the operational meteorological satellite system—the first operational satellite system to emerge from America's civilian space technology effort.

During the past ten years, an estimated one million forest fires have broken out in the United States. Most such fires are quickly discovered and brought under control. Others, however, occur in inaccessible areas or are discovered too late. When this happens, they can do immense damage, as evidenced by the five million acres of Alaskan timber that were destroyed in this manner in 1957. The annual economic loss to the United States from these fires is reportedly $50 million to $300 million. And in fighting these fires, human lives are also lost—127 over a recent five-year period.

As it passes over and looks down upon the earth's surface, the camera- and sensor-equipped weather satellite holds promise of being a talented detector of undiscovered forest fires. In well-populated and frequently traveled areas, the discovery of such outbreaks by human observers in watchtowers and by aircraft reconnaissance appears fairly adequate. In isolated, uninhabited, and unvisited forested regions, such discovery is difficult and not infrequently impossible. The fact that some fires smolder as "sleepers" before bursting into open flame or sending up columns of smoke does not help the chances for early detection.

In July, 1962, the first and, to date, the only detection of an active fire by a weather satellite took place. TIROS III obtained pictures showing the smoke from a conflagration in the Trout Lake region of Canada's Ontario Province.[3]

Visual or photographic detection, of course, becomes a problem when the telltale smoke from a fire is not apparent to the camera. Under such conditions it might be possible to spot the fire through infrared techniques, that is, by sensing the thermal radiation being given off. Ability to do this would depend upon several things, including (1) the intensity of the fire, (2) its extent, (3) the resolution of the infrared sensor, and (4) the presence or absence of clouds.

If a thick cloud system overhangs the area, or if clouds have been created by hot air rising above the burning area, then still another technique would have to be used. TV cameras and IR sensors could not effectively penetrate this blanket of water droplets. The radio waves emitted by the fire might be detectable through the clouds, however, and thus provide the needed detection means. The extent to which this type of radiometry could be usefully applied to fire detection is speculative at this time.

Also speculative but nevertheless appealing to the imagination is the concept of using these same observing techniques, TV, IR, and microwave, to check and report on the relative activity or inactivity of the world's volcanoes. No erupting volcano has been caught in

---

[3] On his orbital flight of February 20, 1962, John H. Glenn took a color photograph of northern Florida that showed smoke plumes from burning brush fires.

the act by a weather satellite. As sensors and routine coverage improve, however, it seems reasonable to assume that someday one will. A picture was obtained of Mount Villarrica in south central Chile by TIROS VII in early March, 1964. The location of this 9,314-foot volcanic peak is marked in the photo by a dark circle, tentatively identified as cinders and ash.

A different and very special type of cloud—the locust cloud—may someday become a major non-meteorological target for the weather satellite's watchful television eye. In certain parts of the earth, the desert locust continues to be both a menace and a plague. Sixty nations spend about $15 million annually in an attempt to control this highly mobile and gregarious insect that likes to travel and infest the countryside in great destructive swarms.

Locust clouds have been observed as small as a half-mile square and as large as 75 miles square. In vertical extent they have ranged from a few yards to several thousand. Some swarms are estimated to have weighed in the thousands of tons. Little wonder, then, that the detection of these insects and the accurate prediction of their movements is of critical importance to governments in Africa and the Middle East which have taken collective steps to stockpile and employ insecticides against this voracious enemy-in-common.

Because desert locust clouds are somewhat comparable in size to conventional weather clouds, the possibility of detecting and tracking them through the use of weather satellites is indeed an intriguing one (Fig. 79).

To date this has not been achieved. Indeed there is some question as to whether their reflectivity is sufficient to be picked up and adequately identified by the satellite camera. But in the future—who knows? Like water-droplet clouds, perhaps insect clouds, too, can be detected by other than visual techniques.

And although no TIROS has yet taken and read out a picture that could be identified as showing locusts, TIROS observations have been useful in combating this insect problem. By supplying weather data for remote and otherwise meteorologically unreported hinterland regions, they have provided valuable information on fronts, winds, and air mass movement—valuable because the large swarms apparently tend to travel downwind.

For what other non-meteorological applications may weather satellites be utilized?

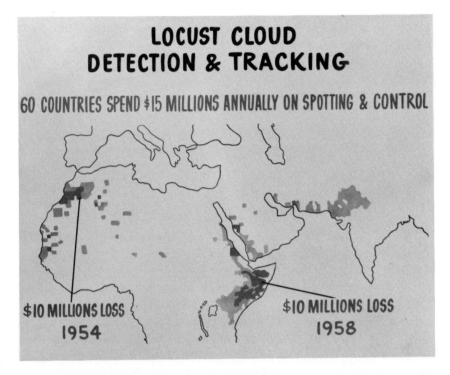

Fig. 79. Applying American weather satellites to locust cloud spotting could bring economic benefits to many nations and constitute a valuable instrument of international goodwill. (U.S. Weather Bureau photo.)

1. Ice reconnaissance (see page 68).
2. Snow-cover mapping (see page 65).
3. Globally observing incoming radiation from the sun and space.
4. Direct or indirect observation of schools of fish.
5. Tracking of icebergs (an individual berg, however, has not yet been identified as such in any TIROS picture).
6. Carrying navigational subsystems so that they might serve additionally as navigational satellites.
7. Mounting a flashing light that can be sighted upon from the ground and used for geodetic measurements.
8. And observing and reporting the state of the sea to maritime operators.

It is an impressive list.

SATELLITE COLLECTORS AND DISTRIBUTORS OF
WEATHER INFORMATION

Over the years a substantial network of weather stations has internationally come into being. Technically advanced countries and those to whom weather is of major importance have established active national meteorological services and have provided them with facilities by which to observe, report, and operate.

Nevertheless, only 20 per cent of the atmosphere is considered to be adequately or even near-adequately monitored by these stations. They are to be found primarily in populated areas. Hinterlands, as exemplified by the interiors of South America and Africa, are only fragmentarily covered. So are the Arctic and Antarctic. As for the oceans, their weather is known by putting together reports received by radio from passing ships, from aircraft, and from certain island stations. Even today there are many areas about the earth where no one ever goes and where information on winds, temperatures, and the like is unavailable.

To meteorologists these regions of unreliable, incomplete, or totally absent coverage are "data-sparse areas" (Fig. 80). A prime concern to weathermen is how to fill the information gaps that such areas represent.

The satellite can fly over these remote parts of the earth and bring back pictures of the cloud cover that exists there. The satellite, however, cannot yet provide quantitative measurements of the conventional type.

To help meet the sparse-data-area problem, at least as far as the shipping lanes are concerned, an international program for obtaining weather information from vessels at sea has been in operation for some years. Today this program consists of about 1,100 merchant ships that take surface-type observations every six hours and report the results by radio.

A similar program, except that it additionally includes upper-air or radiosonde balloon observations, is currently carried out by fifteen United States vessels, each with Weather Bureau personnel on board.

Mid-ocean weather data, surface, radiosonde, and rawinsonde, are also provided by the twelve ocean station vessels, nine in the Atlantic and three in the Pacific, that are maintained through the

Fig. 80. The extent to which the oceans and certain continental areas are meteorologically unobserved is vividly shown by this map of upper-air observing stations. Note the scarcity of coverage in Africa and South America. Even where such stations exist, they are often so far apart that weather disturbances can develop and pass between them undetected and unreported. (U.S. Weather Bureau photo.)

International Civil Aviation Organization. The purpose of these ships is to furnish weather, navigation, communication, and rescue services to transoceanic aviation. The United States fulfills its part of this international commitment by supplying four of the Atlantic and two of the Pacific stations, using Coast Guard cutters, each of which has Weather Bureau observers on board.

To cover marine areas not traversed or observed by surface vessels, a weather sensing buoy, MAMOS, is being utilized. MAMOS stands for Marine Automatic Meteorological Observing Station and is a Weather Bureau adaptation of a similar buoy originally developed by the Navy (Fig. 81). The first two MAMOS units were intended for completion and anchoring in the Gulf of Mexico (an im-

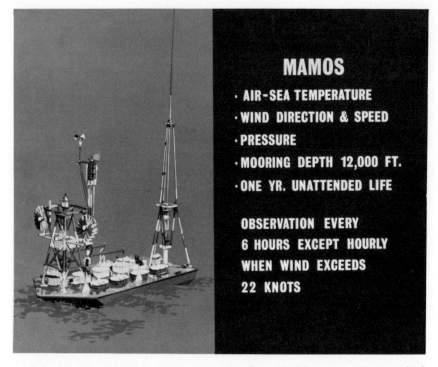

MAMOS

· AIR-SEA TEMPERATURE
· WIND DIRECTION & SPEED
· PRESSURE
· MOORING DEPTH 12,000 FT.
· ONE YR. UNATTENDED LIFE

OBSERVATION EVERY
6 HOURS EXCEPT HOURLY
WHEN WIND EXCEEDS
22 KNOTS

Fig. 81. The Marine Automatic Meterological Observing Station. (U.S. Weather Bureau photo.)

portant area from a hurricane standpoint). MAMOS holds promise as the basis for a buoy network that would provide an oceanic weather watch in sparse-data regions. This is a promise that will grow substantially if to the existing MAMOS capability can be added that of obtaining upper-air information, perhaps by means of small sounding rockets.

MAMOS, without its hull, may see still another application. Just as there is a need for automatically reporting weather in the unobserved ocean areas, so is there one for doing the same in isolated continental regions, such as the far North, the Antarctic, and the jungles of South America. An experimental isotopic-powered automatic land station has undergone tests by the Weather Bureau in the Canadian Arctic. Any large-scale application of automatic weather stations in remote land regions, however, will more probably use a conventional approach, such as MAMOS-type sensors, power supplies, and transmitters, all suitably housed and installed.

Transmission of ship-derived weather information from data-sparse areas is dependent upon radio communications. As is well known, the world's ever-increasing demand for communications imposes a tremendous problem concerning the allocation of frequencies and the volume of radio traffic. Often, the receipt of weather reports from merchant shipping is delayed owing to (1) the traffic, (2) the taking of precedence by other marine messages, and (3) the relaying of the reports by hand-transmitted numerical code through several different points.

To alleviate this communications "jam-up," to expedite delivery of the reports, to eliminate the garbling that relaying sometimes introduces, and to reduce or terminate the costs that the Weather Bureau must pay to commercial concerns for receiving and handling these radioed observations, the concept of collecting them by satellite is under very careful consideration (Fig. 82).

Known as SCOMO (Satellite Collection of Meteorological Observations), this concept additionally visualizes a similar pickup of data from unattended buoys and automatic land stations. In each case the observing platform (ship, buoy, land station, and perhaps, in the future, aircraft) will radio its report to a satellite that, in turn, will pass it on to appropriate weather analysis activities.

Exactly how the satellite will do this is yet to be decided. If polar-orbiting data collectors are used, they will probably interrogate the platforms, receive the weather reports in the form of automatically transmitted replies, store them, and then read their contents out to a Command and Data Acquisition station for transmission to Suitland and further retransmission from there.

If a twenty-four-hour synchronous or "hovering" data collector satellite is used, one that is placed 22,300 miles out from the earth and over a specific point on the equator, then the platforms within its range will communicate their observations up to it for immediate relay back down directly to Suitland or to similar weather information centers elsewhere about the world.

Whether to use polar-orbiting or synchronous data collection spacecraft involves again the matter of observational, technical, and economic "trade-offs." [4] Because stale weather information is the

---

[4] Various orbits can be used for data collection. For brevity, only two are mentioned here.

Fig. 82. A radiosonde balloon being launched by two crew members of the Coast Guard cutter "Owasco" en route to Ocean Station "Delta" in the North Atlantic. The results of soundings such as this may be communicated, at some future time, via satellite pickup or relay. (Official U.S. Coast Guard photo.)

anathema of operational meteorologists, it is essential that the time of reporting or communicating the observations coincide as closely as possible with the time at which they are made. A collection delay is inherent in the polar-orbit approach. The synchronous satellite therefore seems initially the more promising.

In addition to globally collecting the raw observational data, satellites can be expected also to distribute refined meteorological products. Weather maps, coded messages, and other processed weather data will be communicated up to the satellite for broadcasting (1) to the areas overflown by it, in the case of the polar-orbit vehicle; or (2) to the hemisphere within its continuous communication "view," in the case of the synchronous one (Fig. 83).

The idea of placing three synchronous equatorial satellites around the earth and of utilizing them for the worldwide distribution of weather data represents one of the most significant contributions

Fig. 83. The facility maintained by the Weather Bureau's National Weather Satellite Center to receive, process, and analyze the observations made by meteorological spacecraft. (U.S. Weather Bureau photo.)

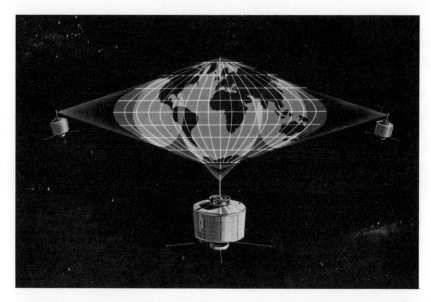

Fig. 84. A visualization of the type of coverage made possible by three synchronous communications satellites positioned over the equator. Owing to the earth's curvature, this coverage does not include the northernmost and southernmost polar latitudes. (Hughes Aircraft Company and NASA photo.)

that satellite technology may someday make to the international meteorological community (Fig. 84). Before this type satellite system can materialize, however, and be adopted by the world's weather services, it must prove its comparable reliability with currently used international teletype and radio circuits, offer adequate data capacity, be economically feasible, and, in general, afford enough advantages to warrant its use.

All in all, there appears little doubt that one of the biggest steps forward to come in satellite meteorology will take place in the communications area.

GROWTH AND DEVELOPMENT OF METEOROLOGICAL SPACECRAFT TECHNOLOGY

To accomplish these observations and applications of the future, weather satellite technology will have to acquire new characteristics and capabilities. The manner in which this takes place will be evolutionary rather than revolutionary in nature. It is improbable that meteorological satellites will become the sudden object of a crash program to improve their usefulness. Crash programs are undertaken, primarily, to initiate activities that are not yet adequately begun.

In satellite meteorology, the activities for the future are already underway in the form of improved spacecraft; new sensors and sensing techniques; higher performance launch vehicles; greater life and reliability; more flexible and useful data processing, analysis, and distribution; and other areas involving the observing, recording, communicating, and utilization of weather information. Some of this work is being performed by NASA; some by the Weather Bureau.

To try out these new ideas and technical developments, NASA will use TIROS and Nimbus.

A future NASA-sponsored TIROS experiment, already publicly announced, would place the spacecraft in a highly elliptical orbit. At apogee, farthest distance from the earth, it would be thousands of miles "up." Considerable information on camera performance and on what the earth looks like from such heights would, of course, be a significant outcome of this experiment.

Nimbus "B," second spacecraft of that lineage, may carry radio-isotopic power sources, a SCOMO-like data collection package, and other experiments that would make use of that spacecraft's considerable payload capacity, growth potential, and earth-orientation.

In addition, there will be tests of gravity-gradient stabilization—a technique of passive attitude control by which gravitational pull is used to orient a non-spinning satellite so that it points earthward —aboard a family of spacecraft called Advanced Technological Satellites. New meteorological cameras or sensors may also be carried by these ATS vehicles.

Still other spacecraft may take aloft nuclear reactors to evaluate their promise as space-borne power sources.

From these and many other experiments conducted on the ground in laboratories and environmental test chambers, in the air with balloons and aircraft, and in orbit aboard spacecraft, new vehicles will certainly evolve. Among them will doubtlessly be a synchronous meteorological observing satellite.

Like the synchronous communications satellite described earlier, this will be a spacecraft placed into orbit 22,300 miles above the equator. At such an altitude, its orbital period, the time required to make one turn around the earth, will amount to twenty-four hours.

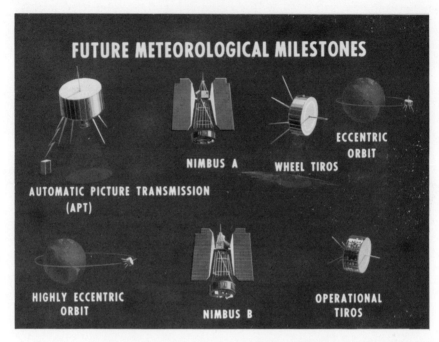

Fig. 85. Highlights of future weather satellite achievements are depicted in this NASA sketch. The TIROS-based Automatic Picture Transmission experiment was successfully carried out December 21, 1963. Nimbus "A" was launched August 28, 1964, and the first wheel TIROS scheduled for late the same year. The fourth quarter of 1965 expects to see the first launch of an operational TIROS in a wheel configuration. (NASA photo.)

Moving thus, in the same direction and at the same angular rate as the earth, the satellite will remain in a fixed position with respect to the earth's surface.

This fixed or "hovering" position will enable that portion of the earth within its camera view to be kept under continuous observation. From a meteorological utility standpoint, this is important; it means that short-lived weather disturbances, tornadoes and thunderstorms, for instance, can be detected and their genesis, development, movement, and dissipation carefully followed. A synchronous satellite would, therefore, provide the means to observe those weather phenomena that, owing to their localized and brief duration, might escape detection by satellites in TIROS- or Nimbus-type orbits.

The value of a synchronous meteorological satellite will extend

far beyond its application to the detection of disturbances for operational usage. It will prove a tool invaluable to research meteorologists [5] who, for the first time, will be able to see the full disc of the
earth as it appears from that distance out (Fig. 86). Owing to the

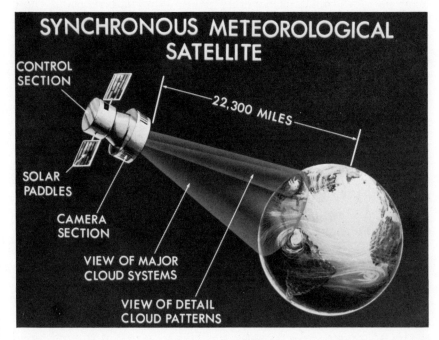

Fig. 86. Synchronous meteorological satellites, as generally visualized, will
observe the earth using two systems, one for broadscale surveillance coverage,
the other for detailed examination of areas of special interest. (NASA photo.)

earth's curvature, effective viewing, that is, the ability to resolve and
discriminate weather details, will probably be limited to somewhere
between 65° North and 65° South latitude.

[5] The role played by research meteorologists in the weather satellite program is
often overshadowed by the more spectacular spacecraft and operational aspects.
Nevertheless it is one of the program's most important. By analysis of the pictures
and data obtained, these researchers provide a better understanding of the atmosphere
and an increased ability to make worthwhile use of the information obtainable through
space-borne cameras and sensors. At the Meteorological Satellite Laboratory, research
arm of the National Weather Satellite Center, about sixty people are engaged in this
type of work. Major projects include (1) investigating the ability to determine
vertical and horizontal air motion by means of cloud pictures, (2) enhancing knowledge of the earth's heat budget, and (3) developing a technique by which cloud
picture information can be utilized in computer-based analysis programs.

To cover the remaining latitudes, essentially the Arctic and Antarctic, supplementary observing satellites in polar orbits would be required. As an alternative, one of the synchronous vehicles—four would probably be optimum for efficient global viewing—might be placed in a slightly inclined orbit so that it pursued a figure-eight flight pattern around its hovering point. This pattern could cause it to meander north and south enough to observe the top and bottom of the globe. It would introduce some complications, however, and upset the clean-cut idealized situation of having equally spaced observing and reporting spacecraft maintaining fixed positions at given longitudes around the equator.

Although the concept of a synchronous meteorological spacecraft was originally planned in 1961 for subsequent implementation as part of the National Operational Meteorological Satellite System, it has since moved forward relatively little toward reality. TIROS and Nimbus have dominated the weather spacecraft program and commanded the bulk of its technical resources and budget.

Certain objections, furthermore, have delayed hardware development of the SMS as this type satellite is now known: (1) it is a highly sophisticated and very advanced concept, representing a substantial and costly technological effort; (2) because it does not basically offer high latitude coverage, its use would probably still necessitate a system of polar-orbiting vehicles; and (3) the short-lived storms that it would detect might be more economically and practicably observed (operationally speaking) by use of ground-based radars set up for this purpose in areas where such storms customarily exist and do damage.

The passage of time and the inexorable march of scientific and engineering progress, however, will eventually bring the stationary twenty-four-hour meteorological satellite to fulfillment, very possibly by combining the observing and communicating advantages offered by vehicles of the synchronous type.

WEATHERMEN AS ASTRONAUTS

Synchronous spacecraft have been occasionally suggested as the end of the technological road, the so-called "ultimate," in weather-observing satellites. This is not so. An even greater and more challenging area lies ahead: the making of meteorological observations

Fig. 87. A model of a synchronous meteorological satellite. (Republic Aviation Corporation photo.)

from manned space platforms. So great are its implications that, like the coming on the scene of TIROS, its realization will begin yet another whole new chapter of meteorology.

The different designs, the size and role of their crews, the problem of human performance and survival, their fabrication or deployment in orbit, the matter of provisioning and resupply—these are but a few of the problems involved in putting space platforms about the earth. They constitute themselves more than enough material for a separate book.

For purposes of this one, however, let us assume that the technology for placing such stations in orbit and for usefully employing and keeping crew members alive aboard them have been worked out. What reasons exist to include meteorologists in these crews? What weather-observing advantages do manned space stations potentially provide?

Essentially, the platform offers a flexibility and adaptability not characteristic of the unmanned weather satellite. By its nature, the latter is limited to basically fixed-type instrumentation and can respond very little to unexpected conditions or phenomena for which it has not been designed to observe.

A classic example, illustrating the advantages of human observers, concerned the "fireflies" observed by Colonel Glenn during America's first manned orbital mission. On the following flight, Carpenter saw the same thing and hit his hand against the capsule side, causing an increased number of these luminescent particles to appear. (They are now thought probably to have been ice crystals.) This established without much doubt, and by the simple use of man's presence, intelligence, and adaptiveness, that the "fireflies" originated from the spacecraft and were not some new and unexplained phenomena of space. Had it not been for the presence of man aboard to find this out, a variety of unmanned experiments would probably have had to be designed and flown to study by automatic instrumentation the nature of these particles and the mystery of their origin. The scientific world was doubtlessly saved a substantial amount of effort, money, and many, many papers and articles speculating upon and describing experiments, completed and contemplated, to solve the enigma of the "fireflies."

Aboard space platforms, meteorologists could:

1. Examine storm-suspect areas or regions of particular weather interest in greater detail by being able to change lenses, filters, and sensors to accommodate the particular situation being observed;
2. Verify observations and experiments being carried out by unmanned instrumented weather satellites, either research or operational in nature;
3. Make use of observing equipment, involving electronics packages, antennas, and the like that would be too large or bulky for unmanned satellites but which could be carried aboard a space platform;
4. Carry out special observations at the request of weathermen on the ground and answer their questions by direct observation coupled with direct communication;
5. Perform on-board data processing and use the results as the basis for determining what to observe, sense, scan, and otherwise look at next;
6. Communicate the processed data to the ground;

7. And maintain, replace, and repair cameras, sensors, communications, and other subsystems to guarantee their continued functioning and high operational reliability (in the case of unmanned vehicles, major equipment malfunctions require replacement of the spacecraft, a substantial factor in terms of satellite and launch vehicle costs).

Such meteorological tasks and others will someday be performed from orbiting space platforms. In themselves these tasks are not urgent enough to warrant the development of such vehicles for this specific purpose alone. When collective national needs result in the creation of these craft, however, their use for meteorological observations will inevitably follow (Fig. 88).

Weather Bureau experiments to photograph the earth's cloud cover were carried out by Mercury astronauts. Additional ones will be performed in the forthcoming Gemini and perhaps Apollo flights.

Fig. 88. Space rendezvous operations of the future—a new meteorological crew reports on board. (NASA photo.)

When the first platforms are placed in orbit, it is not unlikely that a little piece of one or more of them will carry a nameplate that reads U.S. Weather Bureau—that one or more members of the crew will be a fully trained Weather Bureau scientist-astronaut.

INTERNATIONAL UNDERSTANDING AND GOODWILL

Weather is no respecter of political boundaries. It brings alternately to all countries a variety of conditions, sometimes fair and favorable, sometimes stormy and destructive.

Despite his progress in many fields, man has been able to do little to tame the elements and not much more to protect himself against their onslaught. In the face of this atmospheric environment that can so quickly change from friend to foe, the nations of the world have sought assistance through collective action. To provide the machinery for a collaborative program of weather information exchange, a number of them in 1878 established what was called the International Meteorological Organization, an activity that grew in size, importance, and membership. About 1950 it was designated the World Meteorological Organization and made a specialized agency of the United Nations.

Today the WMO includes more than 120 member states dedicated to (1) speeding the distribution and exchange of weather data, (2) expanding the various observing networks and techniques, and (3) standardizing the methods of observing and reporting.

To carry weather information between the participating nations —Communist China is the only large power not represented—an immense communications network links New York, Frankfurt, Moscow, New Delhi, Tokyo, and San Francisco. Over its circuits and its many branches, a round-the-clock flow of the latest weather information takes place. Owing to the scarcity of meteorological reports in the Southern Hemisphere, a similar network has yet to be established there.

This dependence by most of the world's powers upon international cooperation in weather matters has made meteorology an essentially non-political subject. As such it offers opportunities, many of them not yet realized, to improve understanding and goodwill. President Kennedy in particular recognized this and spoke often of achieving better international relations through increased cooperation in weather.

The international benefits made possible by the exchange of weather satellite and other data are not all political, however, or intended solely to reduce world tensions.

Weather information is valuable information to the United States and to all nations, especially those with relatively undeveloped and none-too-stable economies.

It has been estimated, for example, that if the weather could be continuously and accurately predicted only five days in advance, many millions of dollars in savings would accrue to industry, commerce, and agriculture in the United States each year.

Apply these economic savings to the world as a whole and the poor nations in particular; then add to these the special warnings that weather satellites can and may provide regarding hurricanes, typhoons, locust swarms, volcanic activity, undetected fires, or other hazards; and the impact of meteorological spacecraft upon national and foreign policy becomes very clear indeed.

CONCLUSION

The weather is a global phenomenon. The satellite is a global vehicle. These two separate yet related facts explain the origin and spectacular development of satellite meteorology. They apply to unmanned orbiting vehicles and equally to manned orbiting spacecraft.

Their relationship is not limited to this planet alone. It will be made use of on other worlds as well. For in the years to come, weather will be redefined. No longer will it signify just the bottommost part of the earth's atmosphere. Instead "weather" will be considered the environment in which man happens to find himself—regardless of his location within the solar system or without.

Wherever man will go, "weather" will be with him and important to him. To understand and make best use of it, be he on earth, on Mars, or on a planet about some distant star, man will draw upon the techniques and experience first made available by the NASA–Weather Bureau meteorological spacecraft effort of today.

Bibliography

Because *Weather Eyes in the Sky* has been written as a popularized account of America's meteorological satellite program, descriptions in depth and technological details have not been included.

Persons interested in such descriptions and details are referred to the *Bibliography on Meteorological Satellites, 1952–1962,* available from the Superintendent of Documents, U.S. Government Printing Office, Washington, D.C. (This 380-page document lists 988 separate items.)

A frequently updated bibliography, containing later references, is *Publications on Meteorological Satellites by Staff Members,* which can be obtained from the National Weather Satellite Center, U.S. Weather Bureau, Washington, D.C.

Excellent summary presentations are to be found in:

AMERICAN INSTITUTE OF AERONAUTICS AND ASTRONAUTICS. *Astronautics and Aerospace Engineering.* Vol. 1, No. 3, April, 1963. Special Issue on Weather Satellite Systems.

NASA and U.S. DEPARTMENT OF COMMERCE, WEATHER BUREAU. *Proceedings of the International Meteorological Satellite Workshop (November 13–22, 1961).* Washington, D.C.: Superintendent of Documents, U.S. Government Printing Office, 1961.

U.S. SENATE COMMITTEE ON AERONAUTICAL AND SPACE SCIENCES. *Meteorological Satellites.* Staff Report. Washington, D.C.: Superintendent of Documents, U.S. Government Printing Office, 1962.

The only known book on the subject is *Meteorological Sputniks* by K. Ya. Kondratiev (Leningrad, 1963).

Index

Italic page numbers indicate illustrations.